Norfolk & Suffolk
IN THE AGE OF STEAM

Norfolk & Suffolk
IN THE AGE OF STEAM

COMPILED AND EDITED

BY

HOWARD STEPHENS

HALSGROVE

First published in Great Britain in 2004
Reprinted 2008

Unless otherwise acknowledged, the photographs in this book
are from the collection of Bressingham Steam Museum,
Bressingham, Diss, Norfolk, IP22 2AB.

British Library Cataloguing-in-Publication Data
A CIP record for this title is available from the British Library

ISBN: 978 1 84114 216 6

This edition produced exclusively for
LUCAS BOOKS
Churchgate House, Thorndon, Suffolk IP23 7JR
Tel & Fax: 01379 678242
E-mail: info@lucasbooks.co.uk
Web: www.lucasbooks.co.uk

HALSGROVE
Halsgrove House
Ryelands Industrial Estate, Bagley Road,
Wellington, Somerset TA21 9PZ
Tel: 01823 653777
Fax: 01823 216796
email sales@halsgrove.com
website www.halsgrove.com

Printed and bound in Great Britain
by CPI Antony Rowe Ltd, Wiltshire

Foreword

The introduction of steam engines to replace the work of men and women was, as we know, met in many areas of Britain with resentment, violence and bloodshed. But these same machines also relieved the agricultural labourer, and those condemned to work in mills and mines, of a life of unrelenting hardship and a premature death.

While we should forget neither the tragedies nor the triumphs brought about by advances in technology, we must also acknowledge that steam engines today are regarded by many with affection. I believe that much of our fascination for engines powered by steam derives in part from the relative simplicity of their construction. This is not to deny the skill of their inventors, nor the ingenuity required to create them, it is simply that by looking at them we can see how they work.

Man and machine: each is dependent upon the other. Much the same could be said of the heavy horse that preceeded these machines – and perhaps our affection for both resides in this 'fellowship'. Few can say the same about modern machines whose internals lie beyond our instinctive grasp of how things work, and in whose function we play little part other than switching them on.

My first meeting with Howard Stephens coincided with a visit to the superb museum at Bressingham from whose archives much information in this book was drawn. It was in January, out of season, and steam engines of every sort sat brooding in repair shops or stood silently on display like hibernating dragons waiting for a show of fire to bring them back to life.

In producing this work, the author has done just what I'd hoped, breathing life into the Age of Steam in Norfolk and Suffolk.

Simon Butler
The Publisher

A 'Garrett' Showman's engine. Such mighty engines were used to haul fairs around the countryside, from village to village, and then to provide the power, either by belt drive or from the mounted generator, to drive the fairground equipment. Even in the late 1800s, such engines were relatively expensive, perhaps £1000, but today a good Showman's engine, in working order, might be worth £250 000!

Contents

The contribution that steam made to the war effort in 1914–18 was immense, and nowhere more so than in East Anglia. As has often been the case throughout history, war was a wonderful fertiliser for invention. The advance in technology, the development of the steam wagon, and major developments in ship propulsion all gained a new sense of urgency. Communications became very important and steam on the roads, steam to build the roads and steam on the farm to help produce enough food to beat the 'U'-boat blockade were all part of the role that steam played. Ironically, it was its use by the armed services that helped contribute to the downfall of steam manufacturers. The Army, in particular, took on many traction engines during the war but in 1918 these were then released onto the open market at bargain prices and the manufacturers, already fighting against the internal combustion engine, could not compete.

Introduction

The production of steam power was based on the availability of coal, often mined in appalling circumstances. The operation of steam engines was a dirty, tiring and uncomfortable business; there were many dreadful accidents. Sweat-shop factories, workhouses and hard-earned existences were the hallmark of the age. The passing of steam as the primary means of power in factories, mills, farms and transportation should have been heralded as one of the great advances of all time and the escape from the inherently dirty and dangerous Steam Age should have been celebrated as a momentous turning point in our history. Why, therefore, do people mourn the passing of steam and look back with nostalgia and fondness at an age that brought so much that was unpleasant? In short, what is the fascination of steam power?

Steam may have been the supreme form of power for almost two centuries, but even at its height it was an amazingly inefficient way of producing power. Yet, there is an attraction, an enthralment that has lasted from the inception of steam engines

1969 and crowds flock to watch The Flying Scotsman *on the return run from Diss to Liverpool Street.*

The Flying Scotsman.

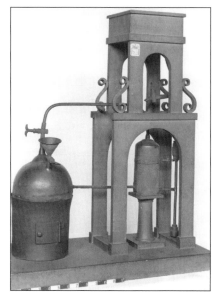

A model of Savery's fire engine. This was the first engine to raise water using steam power.

to the present day. Perhaps it is the paradox that steam presents: steam engines are awesome in their power and yet they are inherently very quiet. To stand beside a working beam engine and watch the great flywheel turn slowly and silently round with just the occasional gasp of escaping steam, is to experience the 'magic' of steam. One can at once sense the power and the amazing genius of the designers who developed these mighty machines, machines that pervaded and dominated every corner of life until superseded by the internal combustion engine.

Those early inventors were genuine pioneers in a new world. They were adventurers whose every step into the unknown was fraught with excitement and danger. It was largely a business of trial and error. Knowledge and the development of science still lagged a long way behind the machinery that was being produced. These inventors cannot have known that if water is boiled the steam created takes up 1700 times more volume than the original water, but they knew that there was power available and they devised brilliant means of harnessing it. Part of our fascination lies in our admiration of those early innovators who created such amazing engines and, without really understanding the science of it, appreciated the potential of steam.

Perhaps also it is that, brilliant though they were, the design of steam engines is relatively simple and can be readily copied by today's more expert model makers. For those whose modelling skills are not up to this, there is an enormous range of static and working models surviving from the Steam Age. It is not just model railways, but a whole range of other steam engines – just look in any toy or model shop.

There were also engineering apprentice pieces built as perfect scale replicas of the full-sized machines. Sometimes an operator would make his own model of the engine that he had driven all his working life. Such models are as robust as the originals and there is an enthusiastic following for steam in miniature. Is it the ability to be a steam-engineer that is the fascination?

Alan Bloom, founder of the wonderful collection of steam engines at Bressingham in Norfolk, believes that the fascination is much more basic than that. Man developed as the supreme being on earth because he learned to harness fire and water. From earliest times these have been vital to the survival and development of mankind. In the steam engine, fire and water are brought together to greater effect than ever before and Alan believes that it is this deep-rooted affair with the elements that is also the root of our fascination with steam engines.

Almost certainly, the answer is that the fascination of steam is a mixture of all these things. Steam still holds a special place in our recent history. It is a timeless fascination. At one end of the scale, young girls and boys, who have never known steam in commercial use, are fascinated by steam locomotives and traction engines. At the other end are the retired drivers and operators who look back with fondness and undying memories of life in the Steam Age.

In many ways we are fortunate that the engineering of the day had to be extremely robust. To build boilers that could withstand the enormous pressures and to build machines that were capable of applying the power that was produced required engineering on a massive scale. An express locomotive can weigh 150 tons or more, a traction engine or a steamroller can easily weigh 50 tons. A single connecting rod from the driving wheels of a locomotive can weigh over a ton. Sadly, as more modern engines superseded the locomotives and traction engines, so

Inside the firebox of The Duchess of Sutherland. *The firebox is placed just forward of the footplate on a steam locomotive and this view shows how the heat from the fire can pass through the tubes and along the length of the boiler, to the smoke box at the front, and then out through the chimney or funnel. The boiler is full of water, at high pressure because it is being heated to boiling point, and every seal has to be perfect. With boilers having to be checked at least every seven years, engineers become very familiar with working in these cramped circumstances.*

A massive Burrell Showman's engine used to haul the fair around the country and then to provide both belt and electrical power when the fair was in operation.

The generations of the Steam Age on the farm.

A Garrett Showman's engine hauling the fair to the next village. Garrett was an important developer and manufacturer of traction and other steam engines, based at Leiston in Suffolk. They produced a number of innovative ideas and although they never really made a success of engines for heavier work, such as ploughing engines, they produced a range of excellent stationary and traction engines and in the 1900s turned their skills to steam wagons. The remarkable history of this firm can be traced in the fine Museum at Leiston, where the history of steam is presented in a most digestible and comprehensive fashion.

many of the steam engines were broken up for scrap. However, those that remain were so massively built that they have survived to the present day in remarkably good condition. In many cases traction engines were simply left in the open in some corner of a yard or farm, locomotives were shunted to the corner of some works and left. One of the engines at the Bressingham Steam Museum was shunted into a disused tunnel in Norway in case it might be needed some day! There it was forgotten until discovered and brought to England by Alan Bloom. The very strength of the engines that the power of steam demanded has been the major factor in keeping so many of these wonderful machines in excellent order today.

Britain was the first nation to produce steam engines successfully and it is in Britain that the finest collections from the Steam Age can be found – many in Norfolk and Suffolk, where steam made its quite distinctive impact. This book traces the Steam Age in Norfolk and Suffolk, setting the developments and changes in these two counties against the backdrop of the development of steam and the Industrial Revolution across the country. In a single volume one cannot possibly give a comprehensive account of every engine and every new development, but some typical examples have been selected and the impact of these developments on the society of the East Anglian counties has been examined.

The Steam Age means many different things to different people. It could be argued that we are still in the Steam Age because many modern nuclear generators use their nuclear power to generate steam that in turn drives the turbines of the generator. However, most regard the Steam Age as starting at the point when steam first became a viable alternative form of power to the horse and the wind, and it drew to a close at some stage between the introduction of efficient internal combustion and diesel compression engines in about 1920, and the end of the steam era on the railways in the 1950s. Of course it has lingered both at sea and in the generator business and even today there are serious attempts to revive steam power using modern technology to make the intrinsically inefficient steam engines much more efficient and using oil rather than coal as the main fuel.

For the industrial heartland of Britain, the Steam Age means that period when the machine brought employment and a strange partnership of prosperity and poverty to areas of the country where both water and coal were readily available. From its early use in stationary engines in the mills and factories, the steam engine gradually spread out to encompass almost every corner of industry, agriculture, fishing, transport, emergency services, construction, demolition and leisure. As the uses grew so manufacturers of steam engines tried to keep pace with the market and hedged their bets by attempting to compete in all fields, but this became more and more difficult. There was an inevitable tendency for different types of steam engine to be developed nearest to their place of use. Thus the tin-mining communities of the West Country gave rise to the Cornish Engine and its successors, designed for pumping water from the mines. It was the availability of both coal and water in the Midlands and Northern England that made those regions the natural choices for mills and factories. Deeper mines required different sorts of pumps and comparatively lighter industrial engines were required to power the factory machines.

It was at the shipbuilding centres along the Clyde that the early developments for sea-going steam power were made. The development of steam engine production in both Scotland and the Midlands acted as a catalyst for the growth of communications and transportation. Extensive rail networks served these industrial regions.

At first sight, Norfolk and Suffolk seem to have been left out of the story. The cotton industry of Norwich was lost to the steam power of the Midlands and there were no natural resources in the region to encourage the development of steam power. It was just an old-fashioned agricultural and fishing region, largely by-passed

by the Industrial Revolution. Even the railway came very slowly to the heart of these counties. It is perhaps surprising, therefore, to look at the famous names in steam and to discover just how many there are from Norfolk and Suffolk. If Lincolnshire were to be added the list is astonishing.

When the railway made its way to Ipswich and Norwich and out into the countryside, it provided a ready means of getting agricultural produce and fish distributed quickly and relatively easily to the London markets and to elsewhere in the country. Ironically, the farmers in particular saw steam as a threat to their livelihood and whilst they welcomed the easier transportation, they also saw it as a potential enemy. It would replace labour on the land and, in opening up foreign markets, it would bring in cheap competition from outside. Although the threats were exaggerated, they were not without foundation. The repeal of the Corn Laws that protected the English market against cheap imports (originally from Prussia) coincided with the new-found ability of the farmers in America to send grain by rail to the east coast ports and onwards to Europe. It brought considerable hardship to the farmers of Norfolk and Suffolk and was one of the catalysts for changing the face of agriculture in the two counties. Nevertheless, it was steam power that provided the means for much of the improved efficiency in farming from milling to threshing, from ploughing to ditching. Steam even transformed worthless land into valuable and fertile agricultural fields by making possible the first effective drainage of the fens.

In industrial use in Norfolk and Suffolk, steam was limited almost exclusively to the smaller applications, water pumps, and machines in breweries, tanneries and other light industry. The counties still abound with the many examples of these small industrial machines, many still maintained with loving care in perfect working order. Much of the heavier industry was in the production of steam engines themselves and famous names were plentiful: Ransomes of Ipswich for agricultural

The agricultural show at Newcastle in 1864. It was at such shows that the East Anglian manufacturers tried to sell the machines. Ransomes of Ipswich are displaying their range of tall-chimney, portable engines at the left of the picture.

70013 Oliver Cromwell *hauls the* East Anglian *to Norwich.* Oliver Cromwell *was one of the famous Britannia Class Locomotives and was built at Crewe in 1951 and was based at Norwich. It ran over 700 000 miles on East Anglian lines, but was redeployed when diesel locomotives took over in Norfolk and Suffolk in 1961. It was overhauled, again at Crewe, in 1967. On 11 August 1968 it was the last steam locomotive to haul a British Rail passenger train. The Britannia Class were famous for their high standards of engineering coupled with simplicity, reliability and low maintenance costs, and yet still capable of doing well over 100mph.* Oliver Cromwell *can now be admired in the locomotive sheds at Bressingham Steam Museum.*

machinery, Savage of Lynn again for agricultural machines and engines, but also for fairground equipment, Burrells of Thetford for traction engines and steam rollers, Garrett of Leiston and Clayton and Shuttleworth of Leiston for traction engines, Ellist and Garood of Beccles for trawler engines and so on.

Speak of steam and the layman will probably think of railways. Although it took a comparatively long time for the railways to cover the counties, the route through Bury St Edmunds and Haughley Junction was to become a key gateway for the mails to and from Europe, via Harwich. Similarly, passengers, cargo and even complete trains were shipped from Harwich and the railway link played an important role in the economy of the region. As almost everywhere else in the land, enthusiasm then outgrew realism and a web of light railways, which could never be cost-effective in the longer term, spread across the heart of Norfolk and Suffolk. At the time they added significantly to the communications available and helped with the distribution of farm produce and even getting children to and from school. Today, scraps of these many branch lines are preserved as part of the tourist industry in the region and they are probably more cost-effective now than they ever were in their hey-day!

Massive driving wheels were well suited to the flat countryside of Norfolk and Suffolk, where there were no really significant gradients.

With engines from Beccles, on the navigable River Waveney, the fishing fleets of Lowestoft and Great Yarmouth grew at a tremendous rate in the mid-nineteenth century. Communication was often easier and faster by water and it is interesting to note that Mr Garrett of Leiston in Suffolk took his factory staff by boat from Leiston to see the Great Exhibition in London in 1851. It was the result of what he saw on this trip that convinced him that Garrett's had to turn their minds to the steam engine.

Steam tractors and steam trucks made road haulage easier and to help facilitate such movement, steam stone crushing and road rolling was developed. Steam engines drove fire pumps and generators.

As these developments took shape, the whole face of Norfolk and Suffolk changed. Communities became more mobile, many of the traditional trades were lost, new trades were introduced, and the structure of society changed to cope with the new order. And yet Norfolk and Suffolk remain essentially rural communities today, and whilst one man might now work a farm that used to provide a living for 20, and a number of the navigable waterways have long since silted up, there are many aspects of life in these counties that remain unchanged.

A few weeks ago in the author's village a neighbour was having his roof re-thatched. It was a damp and windy afternoon and the thatcher had decided that he should spend his time on the ground rather than on the roof. He was preparing his materials. When the neighbour found him, the thatcher was sitting cross-legged on the grass, oblivious to the wet, and was splitting hazel spars ready to bind the thatch into place. It was a timeless scene that might have been set anywhere in the last thousand years.

Of course, much has changed. River craft and the horse, once the essential backbone of the regional transport system, are now almost entirely for leisure or sporting use, but there are still plenty to be seen. The days have passed when every

Some machines were parked in the corner of a farm and simply forgotten. An enthusiast looking around for a traction engine in the 1960s and 1970s could still come across a scene like this, perhaps untouched for twenty or thirty years.

village or community of any size would have its own coach maker, harness maker, blacksmiths, farrier, vet, and feed merchant. However, these trades and skills may yet be found and in many ways Norfolk and Suffolk seem to have ridden the Steam Age wave. It is almost as if it were a craze that came and went. The changes were significant and they had far-reaching effects, but today they are either forgotten or taken for granted.

Steam still plays an important role in the economy of Norfolk and Suffolk. It is a role far removed from the original commercial or agricultural applications and it stems directly from the attraction that steam still has for people of all ages. The steam museums and heritage railways of Norfolk and Suffolk are key elements of the tourist industry. It is something that those early inventors and engineers could never have imagined. Indeed, even fifty years ago, when the last locomotives, ploughing engines and traction engines were taken out of use and sold for scrap, no one really appreciated the need to preserve examples and it was more by luck than any deliberate plan that so many fine examples still remain.

So let us now step into the shoes of those pioneers and explore the development of steam in Norfolk and Suffolk and the environment in which they lived. It is fascinating!

Coming round a tight corner on the A130.

Chapter One
Setting the Scene

When people talk of the age of steam most minds turn to James Watt, George Stephenson and the railways. It is only the enthusiasts who take a broader view of steam and who often refer to Norfolk and Suffolk as 'the cradle of steam'. It is true that steam power was introduced elsewhere in England some time before it came to the fore in East Anglia. However, once the technology was available, the wealth, the nature of the countryside, and the type of the local industries made Norfolk and Suffolk a natural region in which to exploit the new technology and power in a wide variety of applications.

Before looking at how steam power developed and changed the way of life in Norfolk and Suffolk, it is perhaps worth taking a brief look at the region before the Steam Age, and also to look at the general development of the steam engine. It is

A Suffolk farm yard.

only with an understanding of the background that the reasons for the strength of the steam engine industry in Norfolk and Suffolk can be appreciated. It was a particular blend of factors that made the region a natural focus for the development of steam power.

The region of the East of England today consists of six counties: Norfolk, Suffolk, Essex, Cambridgeshire, Bedfordshire and Hertfordshire. However, most people still freely use the term East Anglia to refer to the East of England and, in doing so, they generally mean Norfolk and Suffolk. It is a region of considerable historic importance with much evidence of early settlement. For many centuries the two counties enjoyed considerable prosperity and prominence. In the medieval period it was the most wealthy and populous region of Britain, and a region with strong royal connections up to the Tudor times. By the nineteenth century it had started to develop a holiday industry, catering for those who wanted to get away from the industrial smoke and enjoy the clean fresh air of the long sandy coast. This was the embryo of today's tourist industry that attracts a large number of tourists to the 140 miles of coastline, the Broads and the many historic sites. It was the conditions engendered in the Midland towns by the Industrial Revolution, coupled with the availability of rail transport, which brought people to the East Anglian coast.

Evidence of Neolithic occupation in Norfolk is found at Grimes Graves in Breckland, in the remains of flint mines from this period. After the Anglo-Saxon invasions Norfolk and Suffolk became a part of the Kingdom of East Anglia. The towns of Norwich and Thetford started to develop and by the year AD920 Norwich had a mint. By the time of Domesday (1086) Norwich was already one of the richest and most densely populated towns in England. It developed further and retained this leading position throughout the medieval period. The wealth of the region was founded largely on wool and the wool trade, although the production of cotton cloth and lace became an important part of the Norwich economy. The many fine churches of the region are evidence of the enormous wealth of those times.

Today the economy of the county is still to a large extent based on agriculture with barley, wheat, sugar beet, oats and vegetables being the major crops. There is also a good deal of mixed farming and animal and poultry husbandry for both the meat and the dairy markets. This diversity has long been a feature of the agriculture of the region but for different reasons, as we shall see later, it was the coming of steam that was the prime factor in reshaping the agriculture of the counties. Apart from crops grown in relatively small quantities for the self-sufficiency of the local communities, there was only one key crop: grain. Arable farming was done by hand and with the help of the horse. A farm needed about one-fifth of its land devoted to growing enough feed for the horses and so the productivity of such farming was relatively low. It was also highly labour intensive.

Again for self-sufficiency, animal husbandry was practised on a relatively small scale, although sheep were kept to supply the wool trade, rather than for meat. However, it was a common sight to see herds of beef cattle in the counties. These were not raised by local farmers but were herds driven down from Northern

England and Scotland, to be fattened up on the lush meadows of Suffolk before being taken to market in London.

Along the coastline fishing had always been important, but the ability to move fish overland was limited and most fish were either eaten locally or moved by ship to the Continent or to London. The Broads had yet to be a holiday and leisure destination and the network of waterways were merely convenient cargo routes in what was otherwise a fairly remote part of the region.

Natural resources were far from plentiful. There was no coal and neither was there any stone. Over the centuries most of the building had used clay lump, some locally-made bricks, flint and timber. Breckland and the area around Thetford provided a good supply of timber, but if stone were needed, for the abbeys and cathedrals, it had to be brought in by ship. Thus almost all the main medieval buildings in which stone was used are on what were then navigable waterways. Stone in later buildings was usually that salvaged from a ruined abbey or other major building.

To support the import and export of goods and to allow the movement of cargoes along the coast a good number of coastal and inland ports were required. Few of these remain usable today, but in their time many were capable of accepting quite large ships and the network of waterways carried the distinctive Norfolk keels and wherries and Suffolk lighters inland.

A threshing team on its way to work. As often happens today with combine harvesting, because of the high capital cost of machinery, a threshing team might have contracts with a number of farmers. Laws preventing movement on the roads after 6.00am or before 8.00pm meant that these teams had a long day raising steam, getting to the job and then in the evening getting back to base and preparing the engine for the next day.

It is the commonly-held view, thanks to Noel Coward, that Norfolk is flat. On the basis that there is no smoke without fire, this is partially true, but somewhat unfair on some pleasant, gently rolling countryside and some stunning cliffs along the northern coast. Of the two counties, however, Suffolk has the broader variety of landscape. There are long shingle beaches, the shingle spit at Orford Ness and some large, unspoiled sandy beaches. The crumbling cliffs at Dunwich give evidence today of how the former town of Dunwich, once the capital of the region and effectively the capital of England, was lost to the advance of the sea. There are some deep estuaries where commercial and fishing ports were developed. The centre of the county has low rolling hills and further west the chalk high ground presents a series of open fields. Like Norfolk, the county prospered from early times. The recently restored Saxon burial site at Sutton Hoo, near Woodbridge, shows that wealth has been in the area for a long time.

This prosperity lasted into the eighteenth century, based largely on the wool industry. The fine churches of Suffolk were also built with much of this wealth and the profusion of these grand buildings throughout the county gave rise to the expression 'Selig Suffolk', meaning 'Holy Suffolk'. The term has been corrupted and is now more frequently used in fun as 'silly Suffolk'.

With the demise of the wool industry, agriculture and the associated industries such as food processing and brewing became the cornerstone of the economy. The heathland of the Newmarket area was ideal for horseracing and the training of horses and it is now famous for its racing stables and studs. The county was also famed for its traditional sturdy workhorse, the Suffolk Punch. Few of these magnificent creatures now survive and their preservation as a breed is a matter of considerable concern. Their decline can be traced to the beginning of the Steam Age.

Lowestoft is a long-established fishing port and with increasing trade within Europe both Ipswich and Felixstowe have developed over the last three centuries as major commercial ports.

Given this general setting, it is easy to see why Norfolk and Suffolk took to the age of steam. The need to improve transportation and to make agriculture more productive were powerful motivators and it was into this setting that the steam engine stepped so readily.

Savery's engine. Thomas Savery designed this simple engine which had no moving parts as such, but relied solely on the condensation of steam to create a vacuum and so provide a pump effect.

The steam engine was not an invention from the same mould as the internal combustion engine. The internal combustion engine was invented, developed and brought to a high degree of efficiency over a very short period. The steam engine was developed over thousands of years and to see how this happened it is necessary to look outside Norfolk and Suffolk.

There had been an awareness of steam and some potential uses from the earliest days of man boiling water over a fire. Initially it seems that steam was used to create magical or religious 'miracles'. In its simplest form the steam could be funnelled into a stream and used to sound wind instruments. More sophisticated devices were constructed to operate simple machines, ingenious for their time, but at the very basics of steam technology. The true power of steam could not be harnessed until it was technologically possible to build a vessel that could withstand great pressure and it was possible to construct with sufficient accuracy a cylinder and piston arrangement. Therefore, most of the early applications used the principles of expansion and contraction. The example usually quoted as the birth of steam power in fact used no steam at all but relied on the heating and expansion of air to move water. In the first century AD, Hero described the temple at Alexandria where the doors opened and closed by the use of fire and water. A fire was lit under a tank, which was half full of water. As the air in the tank was heated by the fire, so it expanded and forced the water to overflow through a pipe into an adjacent bucket. The weight of water in the bucket overcame the counterweight and through a system of pulleys the movement was used to open the doors of the temple. When the fire was extinguished the air cooled and contracted, creating a vacuum, which drew the water back through the pipe from the bucket. When the weight of water was less than the counterweight, the movement was reversed and the doors of the temple were made to close.

It was not until the early 1600s that there is much recorded development in the use of steam power. It was in 1606 that Giovanni Battista della Porta, from Naples, described a machine which was similar in nature to Hero's but used the insertion of steam into the tank to force the water out. He also noted that if a container were filled with steam and then upended on to the surface of water, the water cooled the steam, which condensed, and the resulting vacuum 'drew' water into the container. In the 1650s, Otto Von Guericke demonstrated the power of a vacuum using a cylinder and piston arrangement. He pumped air from the cylinder, creating a vacuum and drawing the piston down. In a spectacular demonstration, he set up this piston arrangement so that the piston was connected to a number of ropes. He then invited 20 men to hold the piston back against the vacuum that he created using a basic vacuum pump – they failed!

The commercial application of these discoveries was still some way off and one of the early uses was in France where steam was used to drive fountains in the gardens of the aristocracy.

Captain Thomas Savery, who had started his career as an engineer in the mines of Devon and Cornwall, was one of the first to see practical uses of steam. In 1699 he successfully demonstrated a steam pump, which was later to be used in mills and other industries, and in domestic water supplies to raise water. The pump had no moving parts as such; the cylinder and piston were yet to be introduced into steam technology, but the system relied on the opening and shutting of valves to drive steam into parts of the pump where it would condense and create a vacuum. The atmospheric pressure would then force the water into the vacuum.

At the beginning of the eighteenth century the first practical steam engines started to appear and slowly man was able to adapt some of these to drive pumps and to provide turning power in the newly-emerging factories. As these engines were developed and became more efficient and effective, so the Industrial Revolution gathered momentum, a momentum that was to change the face of agriculture, industry and transport forever. Mechanised agriculture made it possible to farm more efficiently, while railways and shipping made distribution of produce and goods a practical proposition. Ships no longer depended on a favourable wind and reliability combined with speed helped to open up new markets.

The first significant development came in the early eighteenth century from Thomas Newcomen who constructed a more efficient steam pump for the mines. For the first time the pump consisted of a cylinder fitted with a piston, which separated the condensing water from the steam. This was the forerunner of all subsequent steam engines and the basic principle used until steam finally disappeared from the railways in the 1950s. When the cylinder was filled with steam a counterweighted plunger moved the piston to the extreme upper end of the stroke. Cool water was introduced and the steam condensed and created a vacuum. The atmospheric pressure in the mine acted on the piston and caused it to move down the cylinder, and the resulting force lifted the plunger. The first engine that Newcomen built was taken into use in 1712 and was recorded as still working in 1725 when it was reported as being capable of lifting 60 hogsheads of water an hour, the equivalent of about 5.5 horsepower. Given the technology and the machine tools of the time, this was a truly remarkable achievement.

The Newcomen atmospheric engine was used almost unchanged in design until 1769 when James Watt patented a separate condenser and this started a century of almost continuous development and improvement. Watt had been repairing a model of a Newcomen engine when he was struck by the inefficiency of the design and the waste of power that was inherent in it. His answer was to add a separate condenser, which cut out a lot of the heat loss that was built into the Newcomen design. Initially Watt had problems with his condenser both in design and in

Newcomen engine. Thomas Newcomen designed the first piston and cylinder engine. It was the forerunner of all later steam engines and the general principles survived, unchanged, until the end of the Steam Age.

marketing it, but he joined forces with Matthew Boulton who, with his money and his commercial and technical ability, helped turn the idea into a commercial success. Boulton and Watt then enjoyed an almost total monopoly in the manufacture of steam engines for the next twenty-five years. Much of their work was based in the West Country, where they concentrated on the design and construction of mine pumps, but gradually their influence spread and their engines were taken into use in the cotton, corn and malt mills. In 1781, having been urged to be more commercially minded by Boulton, Watt produced a rotary action for the steam engine. This was a 'sun and planet' arrangement.

This was followed a year later by a double-action engine in which the piston worked in both directions. They added a parallel motion in 1784, the centrifugal governor in 1788 and the pressure gauge in 1790. The complete Watt engine had arrived and it was to enjoy a further ten years of virtual monopoly. In 1800 the patent on Watt's condenser lapsed and Richard Trevithick, a Cornishman, introduced higher steam pressures. At Coalbrookdale he introduced an experimental engine, which achieved 145 pounds per square inch and ran safely and efficiently – a major and remarkable advance and achievement. The development of stationary engines continued steadily and they were deployed to an ever-widening variety of uses and to an ever-growing market. Eventually they became known as Cornish Engines and were to be used all over the world.

Steam power even brought its own vocabulary and many everyday expressions are direct descendants from the Steam Age. Expressions such as 'running out of steam', 'full steam ahead', 'a head of steam' and 'steaming along' are all used figuratively nowadays with little thought to their actual origin, but the word 'steam' became synonymous with 'power' during the eighteenth and nineteenth centuries.

Steam engines crossing a drift in the Boer War. Courtesy of The RASC and RCT Association

Chapter Two

The Industrial Revolution in Norfolk & Suffolk

In little over one hundred years, Britain changed almost beyond recognition. The landscape was transformed, as was the whole basis of society. What had been essentially a rural society with a rural economy, became a largely urban and suburban society. The pace of life increased and the pace of change and the scale of invention and development accelerated. There was a surge in population and the cities and towns grew at a rapid rate to house the increasing numbers. The countryside became neglected and although agriculture retained an importance both as a means of feeding the nation and as the backbone of the rural economy, it had lost its ascendancy. The new drivers of the economy were industry and trade both of which demanded an improved transportation network. While the railways spread to every corner of Britain, shipping increased and ports grew to cope with the increasing throughput of goods.

The urban growth was not simply a result of fewer jobs in the rural areas, in fact, for a long while the opposite was true; with the number of jobs in rural areas actually increasing. However both the birth rate and the survival rate rose and this meant that there were many more people to employ. Even with an increased number of jobs in the countryside, the unemployed were driven to the towns such as Norwich and Bury St Edmunds, and to London and the Midlands. It was an era of significant emigration from all over the United Kingdom, but in Norfolk and Suffolk, especially with the coming of the railways, those who could not find jobs in the countryside headed for the towns rather than face the considerable risks and major expense of a long voyage and the uncertainty of life in New Zealand, Australia or Canada. Furthermore, if life in the towns did not work out, it was relatively easy to return home – not so from the other side of the world!

Steam, when it came to the farms, was applied at first to the more static tasks of threshing and machines used in the barns. It was not until the 1850s that the number of jobs started to fall. This was not simply due to the introduction of steam power, but the improving technology made it possible to produce much better tools for cultivating, sowing, hoeing and harvesting, and even with horse-drawn equipment productivity was vastly improved and the need for labour in the countryside declined.

Another major attraction of life in the towns was that it offered some stability of employment. Generally jobs were not well paid, but there was the guarantee of a regular income and possibly some perks such as housing and a small pension. There was also a considerable variety of jobs including work in the major factories and industries: building, cloth production, railway workshops, a growing chemical industry, gas and waterworks, and all the support functions from clerical and cleaning jobs to banking and other commercial services.

A magnificent Burrell traction engine King George V, now restored and preserved. This is a single cylinder agricultural engine. Most of the early Burrell engines were built using the Burrell patent compound system, but towards the end of the life of the company, they merged with Garrett's of Leiston and more use was made of single cylinder engines. Norfolk and Suffolk retain the majority of 'Burrells' now preserved. Photo courtesy of the executors of the late Gerald Dixon

A Burrell engine in the wood yard. Not only did traction engines make it easier to move large pieces of timber around the yard, they were also capable, via a belt drive, of turning a circular saw and mechanised bench sawing came into being. Until then, almost every Norfolk and Suffolk village had its sawpit where teams of at least two men had to work a pit saw by muscle power. The steam engine could do a week's manual work in a couple of hours.

It was a time of rapid expansion, for example the population of the port of King's Lynn expanded in the first half of the nineteenth century to 19 000. Interestingly, however, this remained relatively static in the second half of the century and was only 21 000 in 1901. Norwich continued to grow steadily throughout the century: 61 000 in 1831 to 112 000 in 1901.

Education, or rather the lack of it, was an enormous problem. High birth rates in the towns and a never-ending flow of young people from the countryside looking for work in the towns, meant that there were far too many children for the limited schools. Private education, some of very dubious quality, abounded. There was no proper control and almost anyone who could find a room or two to spare could set up a school and charge anything from threepence to a shilling a week for each child. It is not surprising that the tendency was for children to leave school early and to start to supplement family incomes. Although the employment of children had long been a concern, it was many years before the numbers were reduced substantially. The Factory Act of 1802 was a start, and subsequent amendments eventually became effective in limiting the employment of children. The problem was more acute in the Midlands, with as many as 67 000 children under fourteen working in the mills in the 1870s, and still over 20 000 by the turn of the century. In Norfolk and Suffolk, the numbers were significantly lower with tasks limited generally to cleaning or minor support roles.

A beautifully compact Baldwin traction engine in use on the farm.

If people were attracted by the stability offered in urban employment, they certainly did not have an easier life. A seventy-two-hour working week was the norm in the factories and mills and it was not until 1850 that this was reduced to sixty hours. The normal working day was twelve hours with two hours allowed for meals and possibly an early finish on a Saturday. Meal times came when the machinery stopped but, even so, operators were expected to clean and lubricate the machines during their meal breaks.

When Saturday became generally recognised as a shorter working day, in the 1870s and 1880s, and the rail network had expanded sufficiently, there was both the time and the facility for sport, either to play or to watch. The first professional football teams came into being and the Football League was formed in 1888.

Norfolk and Suffolk lagged behind the remainder of the country in industrialisation. At the end of the nineteenth century one in every four working men and women in Britain was employed in the factory industries, but in East Anglia this was about one in seven, with many still able to find work in the countryside.

Village and rural communities looked very different between the beginning and end of the Industrial Revolution. Before steam the village depended on wind, the horse and bullock for power. Many of the local trades supported the 'power' industry with nearly every village having a blacksmith, farrier, harness maker, carriage maker, feed merchants and a variety of other shops and inns. The communities were to a large extent self-supporting, creating their own internal economy. By the end of the First World War the changes were already evident and many of the traditional trades had gone forever. The roads and railways made it practical to work further away from home and commuting became a feasible option.

The ploughing engine took a long time to develop, but it eventually put the horse out of business. The big problem was that, because of the power required, the engines were too big and heavy to cross the soft ground. It was only when a winch was mounted under the boiler that ploughing became practical. Two engines would work as a team, from either side of the field, pulling the plough back and forth.

Although industry was established in Norfolk and Suffolk, the lack of local building materials, major waterways and other resources meant that the economy of the region continued to rely heavily on agriculture. The presence of coal and fast-flowing rivers made the industrialisation of Lancashire and Yorkshire an easier proposition and so East Anglia lagged behind much of the rest of England during the Industrial Revolution. In fact, the cheaper production of the northern mills took away much of the existing cotton industry from towns like Norwich and centralised the economy even further on agriculture. This did not prevent the development of the East Anglian towns and ports but it was in farming that steam power was first to make a significant contribution.

The advent of steam power followed closely on the heels of a significant downturn in the fortunes of the region. The wars against the French, which had run almost continuously from 1793 to 1815, had meant that traditional imports had been disrupted and there was much more reliance on home produce. The farmers of Norfolk and Suffolk prospered due to the demand for their produce and high market prices. Farms expanded and more and more land was put to the plough. Wheat was the key product, but once the wars with France were over and the European trade routes re-opened, the price of corn fell dramatically and the demand for home-produced grain withered.

There were rapid changes in fortune as landowners and farmers, who had prospered for the previous twenty years or so, now faced vast cuts in income. Agricultural workers formed the major part of the population and the payments of relief to the poor were, by 1818, amongst the highest in England. The escalating bill caused the Government to look at ways of reducing the amount of relief that was paid and in 1834 the Amendment Act created a number of Poor Law Unions each of which had a central workhouse. These were primitive arrangements where the poor where housed and fed to minimal standards and segregated by age and gender for living and sleeping. The system was detested by those who suffered under it. The workhouses were nicknamed 'spikes', reflecting the misery that they brought, but from the economic point of view they worked, almost halving the cost of maintaining the poor. Splendid examples of workhouses, from an architectural point of view, still exist in Norfolk at Gressingham, and at Onehouse in Suffolk. Happily today their use has changed and they are now a museum and a housing complex respectively.

An early portable engine, simple in design and relatively light. The success and reliability of these engines was to inhibit the developement of the self-mobile engine for agricultural use.

The beginnings of the Industrial Revolution saw the introduction of new equipment such as mole ploughs, threshing machines, lifters, and the first portable steam engines. In an area already hit by a rapid decline in agriculture and with poverty and unemployment rife, it is not surprising that the agricultural workers saw such innovations as further threats to their existence. There were many riots and demonstrations. The most serious recorded took place at Brandon in May 1816 when over 1500 armed men attacked a butcher's shop using the slogan 'bread or blood'. The unease was to continue for the next thirty years. The 1830s saw the Swing Riots in Suffolk. These were so called after the authorities received a number of threatening letters under the assumed name of 'Captain Swing'. They organised attacks on farms and on the new machinery, and also on the workhouses themselves.

Offenders were treated harshly when they were caught and there were many deportations and executions but the riots and damage continued, often lighting the night sky across the counties with the flames from haystacks, barns and farms.

A further complication and cause of discontent was the Law of Settlement and Removal. Parishes were largely responsible for their poor and it was clearly in their interests to limit the number of poor moving into the parish. In parishes where the land was in the ownership of just a single landholder, 'close' parishes, it was possible to apply restrictions and to prevent any ingress of settlers. In the 'open' parishes, where there were several landowners, it was simply impractical to apply the same controls. The result was that these parishes faced much heavier demands for the relief and housing of the poor and there grew a marked contrast between the close parishes and the open parishes. In the former, the landowners had sufficient funds to maintain the cottages and property in good condition, but in the open parishes, where the population was expanding, the greed of landowners combined with impoverished parish resources produced housing of a low and poorly maintained standard. Although the wretched housing around places like Bury St Edmunds has long since disappeared, the evidence of the close parishes remains to this day and can be seen in estate villages such as those at Euston, Somerleyton, Culford and Helmingham.

The effect of the restrictive practices of the close parishes went beyond the housing and support of the poor. Because the close parishes would not accept new residents, it was often the case that those who worked in such a parish actually lived in a neighbouring open parish, walking to work across the parish boundary. This meant that not only was the landowner in the close parish getting cheap local labour, but that he was not having to pay for the housing and upkeep, the responsibility for which fell to the open parish. Some landowners even went as far as demolishing cottages in the close parishes to reduce the number of properties that could be occupied, and so reduce their outgoings.

In the first half of the nineteenth century the population of Norfolk and Suffolk increased by some 60 per cent. In some areas this figure rose to over 70 per cent. Initially this growth in population had a reduced impact on the counties because many families, driven by the decline in agriculture, moved to the industrial areas of England to seek work. The 1851 census reveals, for instance, that over 50 000 people

Steam ploughing could be a dangerous business, and the stress put on the cable could be enormous. There was little protection for the driver if the cable snapped and as soon as a cable started to 'sing' urgent action was needed. If the driver was not fast enough he would be lucky to escape with serious injury. Several were simply sliced in half.

who were born in Suffolk were then working and living elsewhere in England. However, the Industrial Revolution brought increased mechanisation. The reduced opportunities for employment elsewhere, combined with population growth, meant that the people of Norfolk and Suffolk either looked to the Colonies for a new life or tended to stay put and to try to make their living at home. This lead to the growth and overcrowding of the towns and miserable conditions are recorded in Bury St Edmunds, Norwich, Diss, Ipswich and Stowmarket, and elsewhere.

At the same time, and despite having their slum areas, the towns of the region began their transformation into major centres of commerce. Population from the mid-1800s onwards became more concentrated in the towns than in the rural areas and Ipswich was already established as a leading industrial town. Cromer, Lowestoft and Great Yarmouth were developing as major fishing and commercial ports and several smaller towns such as Newmarket, Leiston, Haverhill and Brandon, had a successful industrial base.

The crowding of the towns and the coming of public transport in the form of the railways helped to establish the beginnings of the tourist industry in Norfolk and Suffolk. Felixstowe became a bustling and increasingly popular resort, while Cromer, Great Yarmouth and many smaller resorts along the coast were established as holiday destinations.

A restored steam excavator being put through its paces.

The agricultural decline continued and it was only a few of the more enterprising farmers, those who already had considerable reserves, who weathered the storm and managed to diversify, within the agricultural base. Arable farmers turned to mixed farming with sheep and pigs becoming important. There were also some interesting initiatives such as that set up by John Gurdon. Gurdon was a Suffolk landowner and he selected 20 local men and allowed them to form a co-operative and to rent 100 acres of his land. He provided the start-up capital and the co-operative became a rapid success, paying back the costs in the first ten years and generally improving the living and lot of those who were a part of the enterprise.

Another significant advance was the introduction of allotments. The system began in the 1820s and Professor John Henslow, the Rector of Hitcham, was a driving force in getting the idea adopted and expanded. Allotments provided families with the means to grow some produce for themselves and over the next fifty years the number of allotments in Norfolk and Suffolk grew to about 30 000.

Meanwhile machinery and new techniques made it possible to manage larger farms with improved productivity. Smallholdings were absorbed into larger farms and the area went through a period of what was called 'high farming'. In the twenty years or so after 1850, agriculture once again prospered, although not without opposition from those who mourned the loss of the smaller farms and fields. However, the period was brief and farming was heading for another major fall. The summer of 1879 was one of the worst on record and the crops failed disastrously all across the region. American grain was now being imported and sold at a competitive price and as the quality and quantity of home produce fell so the American supplies flooded in. Norfolk and Suffolk were hit hard and many farmers were forced out of business. The value of property plummeted and farms, which had become uneconomical to run, fell into disrepair and neglect.

Putting the cover over the cab for a rainy day.

The falling level of wages led, in 1872, to a confrontation between the employers and farm labourers. The employers formed themselves into a Defence Association, while the farm labourers flocked to the National Agricultural Labourers Union. The employees demanded wage increases and as the temperature of the debate rose, so, in early 1874, the Defence Association of employers literally locked out the Union members. The dispute started near Newmarket and spread rapidly across the region. Eventually the Union and its members, unable to support their continued action due to shortage of funds, were obliged to forfeit their demands and return to work at harvest time. The Union, which had attained a position of some power and influence, was now irrecoverably weakened and eventually disbanded.

Against this very troubled agricultural backdrop, the mechanisation of farming continued apace, with Norfolk and Suffolk well to the fore in this process. By the mid-1800s there were foundries across the two counties, with 20 in Suffolk alone. Some of the famous names began to become established: Garrett's produced steam engines and threshing sets at their new works at Leiston; Burrells were producing steam engines of all types at Thetford; and Savage at King's Lynn was producing both commercial steam engines and also developing their name in leisure equipment with the construction of some remarkable and robust fairground equipment. Smythes produced seed drills and other machinery at Peasenhall, and Ransomes developed an enormous factory site alongside the River Orwell at Ipswich, where

A Showman's engine built by Garrett's of Leiston.

A Burrell on the early run to work.

they produced a wide variety of agricultural equipment. They eventually joined forces with the Leeds firm of Fowler to produce ploughing engines and they also built railway equipment.

It is ironic that with this wealth of machinery around them, the Norfolk and Suffolk farmers were slow to embrace mechanisation. Seed drilling was still almost exclusively a hand operation until well into the second half of the century. Hand scythes were still preferred to harvest the wheat and corn and hand flails were used for threshing.

Early attempts at mechanisation tended to be simple and the first threshing machines used in Norfolk were powered by hand. In a generally poor economic situation, cost was one consideration, the fear of unemployment another, and also the inherent conservatism of the local farmers. Horse-drawn machines gradually replaced the labourer and by the end of the century steam-driven threshing sets and ploughs were in wide use. But the horse and hand-tools survived until well into the twentieth century.

The mechanisation of agriculture, increased mobility and the coming of the roads and railways required an industrial base to provide the necessary support. Farming remained the prime activity but industry became increasingly important. Some of the older trades were still required and most villages retained their blacksmith and wheelwright. Mills driven by steam provided more reliable service than the weather-dependent wind and water mills, and they were more powerful and productive. Milling became concentrated into fewer steam-powered mills with only a handful of windmills working seriously after 1900. A century before there had been over 1000 across the region.

Over the same period the number of maltings was halved and the breweries diminished by 75 per cent. In their place a number of other industries grew. Some, such as the fertiliser industry, were related to the traditional occupations of Norfolk and Suffolk but others, such as gun-cotton and early plastics, were innovations. But even the new industries did not arise by chance; the many flint buildings of Norfolk and Suffolk tell of the profusion of flint in the area and Brandon was the most important centre in England, if not in Europe, for the manufacture of gunflints. It was perhaps a natural progression to move on to gun-cotton – an occupation not without danger as a fearful accident in Stowmarket in 1871 proved.

Nor was the world of literature and the arts forgotten. Printing became especially important in Norwich and also at Beccles, Diss and Bungay. Straw plaiting grew around Lavenham and silk, linen and cotton weaving, along with horsehair and fibre weaving, became well established in southern Suffolk and along the River Waveney. The skies and coast of north Norfolk, and the unique countryside of what is now called 'Constable Country', attracted artists and the early photographers.

It was not simply the power of the traction engine that made such an impact, it was its versatility. It was an all-weather tool. It could haul, saw, thresh and plough. This machine was built primarily for road use (note the low-slung design suitable for use on roads but not on the farm). Nevertheless, it could be harnessed to an array of other belt-driven tools to carry out a number of functions.

Both counties benefited from their extensive coastlines. As steel replaced timber, so the shipbuilding industry at Ipswich went into decline; but boat building was still a major industry at Woodbridge, Aldeburgh, Beccles, Lowestoft and Orford. There was an important salt-refining plant at Southwold, as well as a successful brewery, and Woodbridge was a major port for coastal shipping. However, the most significant development along the coast during the nineteenth century was the development of the fishing industry, for which Lowestoft was the main centre. In the mid-1800s there had been about 80 drifters based at the port but by the end of the century there were over 400 drifters and, with the advent of trawling, over 300 trawlers.

To link all these industries together and to provide a means of moving raw materials and the distribution of finished goods, it was necessary to have an effective communications network. Up to the eighteenth and early nineteenth centuries movement had been confined to horse-drawn wagons and to the waterways. It is difficult to believe today that some of the ditches that feed the tiny River Gipping were once waterways carrying barges with goods to and from the port at Ipswich. Similarly, canals and cuts off the Broads, which can no longer be used even by the smallest pleasure boats, were once the vital arteries that took produce to market. Even the silted ports of the north Norfolk coast nowadays reluctantly betray their commercial past.

Local trains such as this, often with goods wagons attached, provided a communications infrastructure that helped to open up the 'interior' of Norfolk and Suffolk. Agricultural produce became easier to distribute and light industrial sites grew as both the raw materials and the finished products could be moved about the counties.

The nineteenth century saw the development of such ports to cater for the larger ships, but it was the railway that was to open up the counties and make the industry sustainable. It took a long time for the railway to stretch as far as Norwich, but once it did a whole network of feeder lines was added and the counties were criss-crossed with a network that served not only industry, but also the ports and the ever-more important resorts.

As elsewhere in England, the Industrial Revolution was to change the face of Norfolk and Suffolk forever. However, in these eastern counties economic change was already being forced upon a suffering agricultural community. The repeal of the laws that protected home-grown corn against imports, the increase in imports after the Napoleonic Wars, the fall in wages, prices and land values, all combined to force change upon the region.

Steam power and its associated developments also played a huge role in reshaping the economy and way of life of these counties. If it was slow to take off in an area where industry and prevailing conditions seemed to be ideal, it was not through lack of opportunity or skills, or even money, rather it was the social conditions of the time that proved to be the biggest obstacle.

Chapter Three

Agriculture

I n spite of the ever-increasing application of steam for all manner of tasks, the employment of steam power on the land did not occur until towards the end of the Industrial Revolution. Use in mines and mills had started as early as 1760 but a century later agriculture was still driven by the horse. The railways, ships and factories were all becoming highly mechanised, with agriculture being the poor relation. The main problem was that steam engines were large and heavy. They needed a substantial base from which to work. In the factories this was the stone floor, in the mines it was the rock, in the ships, the strength of the hull, but the soft workable soil on the farms was not the right environment for a heavy engine. It was not that there was a lack of will or desire, simply that no one could find a way of getting round the problem of providing a solid base from which to work while maintaining a tillable soil in which to raise crops.

There were also social problems in that the Industrial Revolution had relegated agriculture in importance resulting in considerable poverty in the countryside. Jobs were hard to find and farm workers were scared that the introduction of mechanisation would create further unemployment. There were many demonstrations and

A Robey portable engine at work threshing. Note the size of the team needed to keep up with the pace of steam thrashing.

riots in which considerable damage was caused and haystacks were burned in protest at the idea of introducing steam power to the land.

Eventually in the late 1860s the first engines were seen in use on the farms of Norfolk and Suffolk. These were portable engines on wheels, which could be moved from one place to another but which had no means of motive power of their own. Horses or bullocks were needed to move them about and their use was very much limited to the activities away from the fields — threshing, corn-milling, and chaff-cutting.

The first practical engines were based on the design of railway locomotives, with the horizontal, multi-tubed boilers, which had proved so successful. However, the farm tracks were rough and good ground clearance was needed, and so the engines were designed with the cylinders mounted above the boiler rather than below.

Because the portable engines were primarily agricultural machines, their manufacture was very much tied to the farming regions, and firms such as Youngs of Diss, Ransomes of Ipswich and Garrett's of Leiston were the important producers.

Compared with railway locomotives they were simple in design. It remained an aspiration to make them self-mobile but the technology was not available. It seemed an insuperable problem because mobility required extra power and working parts on the engine and this made the engine heavier and less able to cope with progress over soft ground.

There were some ingenious but impractical attempts to overcome the difficulties. In 1814 Mr Tindell had tried to introduce a machine that had mechanical legs to push the engine forwards, while a similar experimental machine was produced by David Gordon in 1824. The most spectacular failure was in Devon, where John Heathcoat produced a machine, which had canvas tracks — a forerunner of the tank with its caterpillar tracks. It had a winch fitted and was demonstrated pulling a plough across a field. It was put to use on an area of peat and after two days'

Early portable engines.

Three generations of farmers pose in front of a mill-used portable engine.

A Burrell portable engine, c.1885.

The walking digger as built by T.C. Darby of Chelmsford.

work it was left out overnight. The next day it had disappeared, all 30 tons of machinery had been swallowed up by the peat and Mr Heathcoat was some £12 000 the poorer.

Ransomes had several abortive starts before they produced a workable portable engine. In 1842 at the Royal Show at Bristol, they demonstrated an engine with a vertical boiler. They were awarded a prize of £30 for innovation but failed to sell a single machine. They tried again in 1849, introducing an engine with a horizontal boiler, but the cylinders were mounted under the boiler and this proved no more successful.

The key problem was still weight and in 1846 James Boydell patented a new type of wheel, which had hinged flaps of wood that fell into position and helped spread

Boydell's ingenious 'flip-flap' wheels.

Early traction engine design showing that the steering problem had not been solved. This needed an operator at the rear and a steersman at the front.

the weight of the engine. The system worked but it took another nine years before it was put into use. Once it was seen to work several manufacturers adapted their designs to use Boydell's 'flip-flap' wheels. However, there were still serious drawbacks. For instance, steering was accomplished by a steersman with a sort of tiller arrangement working in front of the machine, or by the use of a horse in shafts. In either case it was a pretty dangerous occupation!

The other problem was that the engines were very expensive and, at a time when agriculture was in crisis and farmers were impoverished, few could afford such machines.

Meanwhile the portable engines were forming an efficient partnership with the new range of threshing machines. If the problem of mobility could be solved and the horses made redundant, it would be so much better. Thomas Aveling adapted an existing Clayton portable engine and put it to use in 1857. The design of the portable engine was such that the cylinders were mounted above the rear wheels from where they transmitted power to the flywheels at the front. To make this self-mobile a chain was fitted from the flywheel shaft back to a sprocket on the rear wheel. This was a much cheaper solution than Boydell's 'flip-flap' method; portable engines now cost not much more than £100.

The idea of the chain was taken up. To prevent stretching and breakage it was important to try to design the engine with as short a chain as possible. This led to the design of an engine with a drive sprocket on the crankshaft, just above the rear wheels. Steering remained a problem and the tiller or horse options were used until well into the 1860s when at last the use of a simple gear and chain method of steering became the norm.

It was John Fowler, based at his works in Leeds, who really achieved the break-through in steam ploughing. He used a portable engine to draw a plough backwards and forwards across a field, and the first major milestone was achieved at Nacton in Suffolk in 1856 when, using this method, he managed to plough an acre an hour. Steam ploughing had arrived.

The basic attraction of steam ploughing was that ploughing by horse was a long and tiresome occupation. To plough an acre of land the ploughman had to walk at least eight miles at a speed of no more than one-and-a-half miles per hour. If the farmer had a 50-acre farm, he had to walk over 400 miles just to plough it, and then

A complicated and apparently heavy solution. The assembled audience look sceptical. (As seen by the London Illustrated News)

A steam-ploughing demonstration in 1856.

A versatile and relatively cheap little engine that could be put to a multitude of uses around the farm: hauling, sawing, thrashing, cutting, grinding, winching or ditching.

With all the weight near the back, such ploughing engines had a tendency for the front to slew and the cable would chafe against the wheels. To prevent this farmers would drop the further front wheel over the rim of a ditch.

It is easy to see why these 'beasts' were not popular on the roads. They were noisy and dirty, they scared the horses and the enormous back wheels could soon make a mess of the strongest of road surfaces. The law was that there had to be someone on foot walking 60 yards ahead of the engine, to warn of its approach and to help calm any horses that they met.

he had to sow, cultivate and harvest. Threshing was powered by horse and the whole routine of life on the farm was geared to what could be achieved by man and horse. The horse had to be rested after a few hours' work and it had to be fed and watered throughout the year, not just when it was needed to work. Ironically, in the early days of steam on the farm, the horse became busier, because greater acreage could be ploughed and therefore there was more planting and cultivation to be done. Furthermore, as we have seen, the early steam engines were not self-mobile and needed horses to drag them around the farm.

By 1880 there was a large production of agricultural engines and among the top twenty manufacturers in England it is interesting to note that nine of them were based in East Anglia. The important manufacturers in Norfolk and Suffolk were Burrell's at Thetford, Garrett's at Leiston, Ransome at Ipswich and Savage at King's Lynn. The price of a portable engine remained at about £100, but to buy a self-mobile engine capable of threshing and haulage work could cost well over £500. Price depended largely on power. Refinements were available at additional cost – double cylinders, sprung suspension, a differential back axle – but farmers seldom bothered to pay out for these 'extras'.

Work in the wood yard might include hawling trunks about, sawing, chaffing or haulage to and from the yard.

A single-cylinder farm engine might weigh about ten tons and the boilers were designed to operate at pressures of 100 to 150lbs per square inch. They normally

An 1875 Robey engine driving a threshing machine. Note the typical home-made water cart to keep the engine topped-up.

had two gears, which gave speeds of two or four mph and it took two to three hours from cold to raise the steam to working pressure. Since much of the farm work, threshing, wood chaffing, sawing, was repetitive and simply required the engine to be put in place and to run, it was desirable that the operator could leave the engine to operate by itself. Such engines were fitted with a safety valve, pressure gauge and water pump, with a gauge glass to show the water level in the boiler. They were also fitted with a governor, which provided automatic control of the speed. The driver could set the throttle fully open and the governors, with their weighted arms opened out by centrifugal force, maintained the required speed by restricting steam inlet into the cylinders.

When the steam engine was being used to drive another machine using a belt, its driving wheels were put out of gear by moving a catch on the main shaft and sliding the driving wheels away from the wheel drive. To change gear the motion had to be brought almost to rest. There was a means of disengaging the driving wheels on the axles to allow tight turns to be made, and also to allow use of the winch without the driving wheels turning. The power available from the winch was awesome, and it could be used for self-recovery from boggy ground, to help climb slippery steep slopes, to pull down trees and, as late as the Second World War, to help in the demolition work of bombed houses.

Fowler developed his ideas and produced an elaborate single-engined system for ploughing. The engine had two cable drums. One would draw the plough out across the field to an anchor cart on the far side, and the second drum would then draw the plough back. One of the advantages of the steam plough was that the basic power available was such that a much deeper plough could be used and this was hugely more effective at ridding the ground of deep-rooted weeds. British steam engineering at this time was the finest in the world and thus British farming became very efficient and profitable.

Belted up and ready to work without supervision.

Various other attempts were made to design an effective steam ploughing system but it was not until John Fowler discarded the original idea, of using a single engine and an anchor cart, and used two engines, that there was any successful development. Although other manufacturers tried to emulate his success, the Fowler engines outsold and outperformed all the competition. A pair of 20-ton ploughing engines could plough 15 to 20 acres in a day, double this if they were only cultivating rather than ploughing. Nevertheless, from the workers' point of view it was a long hard day.

Such engines were still very expensive and few individual farmers could afford them. Most of the work, therefore, was undertaken by specialist contractors on a piecework basis, using a four- or five-man crew. Even so, by about 1900 there were over 600 recorded ploughing sets at work in Britain.

An anchor cart and engine. Courtesy of the Road Locomotive Society

This page and opposite: Steam ploughing in action. Note how exposed the plough operator is if a cable snaps.

Driver's view from the footplate of a Fowler Ploughing Engine Class AA7. It was built in 1917 for the Agricultural Branch of the Ministry of Munitions and is one of a matched pair owned by Bressingham Steam Museum. It was the disposal of large numbers of engines such as this after the war that made them affordable to many farmers for the first time and helped contribute to the decline of traction-engine manufacture.

A Burrell ploughing engine seen here operating a mole-drainer.

To some extent Fowler was a victim of his own success. In 1880 he developed a much better, more powerful and more economical compound ploughing engine, but his earlier machines were so reliable, well made and durable that they lasted too long! Both farmers and contractors were reluctant to throw away perfectly serviceable machines in favour of the more modern version. In fact it took over thirty years for the changeover to gather pace.

The earlier steam engines were hungry and thirsty beasts and when coal prices started to rise dramatically towards the end of the First World War, this was the catalyst for the widespread adoption of the more economical machines. The end of the war also opened a flood of ex-government machines on to the market at much more affordable prices. In the 1920s it was a common sight to see contractors' equipment lying rotting as the contractors were forced out of business by the increasing ability of the farmer to buy his own machine.

Ploughing with such power and to greater depths than had previously been possible required a specialised plough. In 1785 Robert Ransome, then of Norwich, patented a special process to produce hardened cast iron. In fact, like many inventions, the discovery was by chance. Ransome accidentally spilled molten iron from a mould on to a cold floor and he noticed that the cooling effect produced a harder casting.

In 1803 he moved to Ipswich and patented a method of applying a hardened case to ploughshares. In the manufacturing process he chilled the underside of the share to make the surface hard. The top was left unhardened and this had the effect of producing a self-sharpening share. It was the adoption of such shares and the improved strength of the castings that helped make steam ploughing a viable operation.

Keeping up a good supply of water was also a major problem and the fields of Norfolk and Suffolk abound with small ponds that were dug to provide water for the ploughing engines.

Taking on water.

Even with experienced, professional crews, steam ploughing was a difficult operation. The engines were powerful enough to draw a nine-blade plough across a field but there was a tendency for the engine drawing the plough to slew. Telltale marks can be seen today on the surviving ploughing engines. Deep grooves seen on the edges of the front wheels are evidence of where the engine was drawn round by its own power until the ploughing cable chaffed along the wheel's edge. To overcome this the drivers would try to drop the far front wheel into the side of a ditch – a practical solution but, with the rear wheels being set further apart than the front wheels, this did lead to a number of awkward recovery jobs if the driver misjudged his line!

The work was also highly dangerous. By today's standards the engines and machines were death traps. There were no guards around the gears, working mechanisms were exposed, providing plenty of opportunity to chop off a finger or even a hand. Boiler explosions were not infrequent and cable breakages decapitated several farmers. This was a particular danger during ploughing when, if the long cables snapped, they snaked back at terrifying speed. A cable when stretched to near breaking point starts to emit a hum and there was a saying that if the cable starts to 'sing', run for your life. The problem with ploughing cables was that they were so long, and there was little chance of running far enough before the cable gave way.

Danger from steam, hot metal, cogs, wheels and cables.

Boiler explosions occurred sometimes because of a manufacturing fault, especially in the early boilers, but also because drivers wanted to get extra power from their engines and would screw down the safety valve to achieve this. A major accident occurred at Watlington in Norfolk in 1867 when an engine belonging to James Faile exploded. James, his brother and several others were killed in the blast.

A Ransome Compound engine on its way to work.

As if the work was not hard enough, there were other problems facing the agricultural contractors. Not the least of these was moving the engines around the countryside. The Locomotives Act of 1861 provided a general exemption for agricultural engines from road tolls, but they were often limited to travelling on the main or turnpike roads between midnight and 6am, and heavy fines were imposed if these time restrictions were broken, even by a few minutes. In common with other vehicles, ploughing and agricultural engines were limited to two mph in built up areas and four mph elsewhere. A flagman with a red flag was required to walk 60 yards in front of each engine. Ploughing engines were allowed to move in pairs with a single flagman.

These restrictions remained in force until the Highways and Locomotive Act of 1878 eased the movement restrictions and dispensed with the need for a red flag, presumably because the engine itself was more visible than the flag! However, it was still a requirement to have a man walking ahead of the engine to help calm any horses that they met along the road.

Ploughing did not provide the contractor or the crew with year-round work and so other tasks were often undertaken by them. Threshing was one such task. Steam threshing saved on manpower and horses but it still needed about a dozen fit men to man the thresher at harvest time. The farmer had to pay about £5 a day to hire the threshing set, for which he had also to provide the coal and water as well as pay his additional workers. Nevertheless, it was an efficient process and the grain loss during steam threshing was considerably less than that experienced today with

A threshing team (with helpers) on the road.

Maintenance in the contractor's yard.

An early competitor as Ransomes moved into the lawn-mower market.

modern combine harvesters. There will still be people alive who remember the familiar rumble of the metal wheels of the threshing machine as they trundled to and from the scene of the harvest.

Ploughing engines were also ideally suited to the dredging and maintenance of lakes and ponds. A mud scoop would replace the plough and the principle was otherwise the same, with an engine on either side of the lake or pond. Records at Great Ellingham, in Norfolk, show that as late as 1935 this was the method used to dredge some 2000 cubic yards of mud from a pond.

Although steam had its attractions, often the land was simply not firm enough to support the weight of a steam engine and, here, horses continued to be used in parallel with steam engines until the arrival of the internal combustion engine and tractors. Only then could farmers safely discard their horses and open up for commercial use the 20 per cent of their land previously given over to the production of horse feed. Steam came into its own for ploughing heavy soils and clay, or if it was necessary to plough the land deeper than the horses could manage.

There was little further development of the agricultural steam engine until Garrett's of Leiston produced a versatile steam tractor in 1915. It was called the 'Suffolk Punch' but it was really too late as, by that date, the internal combustion engine was starting to take over. By the 1930s almost all steam-engine production had ceased, but the resilience of these machines was such that many were in use until well into the 1940s, some of them being well over fifty years old by then.

Compared with the other areas of steam usage, agriculture enjoyed its benefit for a relatively short period. Sadly, many of the remarkable engines were broken for scrap when they were replaced by the internal combustion engine, but in those remaining it is still possible to appreciate the impressive power of the engines and the skills and ingenuity of the designers and manufacturers. Fortunately, the history of the engines and their use has been well recorded on film.

Threshing teams at work.

A pair of ploughing engines dredging a pond.

to produce. They were also labour intensive to operate because there were no automatic valves, and to make the engine work repetitively it was necessary to open and close a number of hand valves to let in the steam and water at exactly the right moment. It must have been a strange combination of stamina, engineering and bell-ringing skills to ensure that everything happened at the right moment throughout the operation.

Neither were these machines cheap to run and, for instance, there are records of a pump installed at the Walker Colliery near Newcastle, that show it needed six-and-a-half tons of coal each day to operate the pump!

For these and other reasons, steam was slow to come to industry. From the introduction of the early steam engines, the monopoly for steam-engine construction was held by the firm Boulton & Watt, and it was not until 1800 that this monopoly was broken. A major factor was the prodigious output of Watt himself. He brought in innovations and improvements so quickly that by the time another firm tried to copy one of his engines, it had already been superseded. In the period from 1775

A Boulton and Watt pumping engine preserved at Kew Bridge.

to 1785 alone, Watt patented seven new steam-engine designs. Such engines were expensive and any firm looking at the introduction of steam power needed good capital backing. Few could afford to tie up such relatively large sums.

Because of the Boulton & Watt monopoly, it is quite easy to track the distribution of steam engines in industrial use up to 1800. The details are all retained in the records of that company. Not surprisingly, these engines were used in the mines and in the milling and industrial areas that were close to both water and coal. The exception to this was London, but here there was a well-established coal supply coming from the North East, brought up the Thames Estuary to the coal wharves.

The records of Boulton & Watt do not record a single engine in Norfolk or Suffolk, although there were up to 4000 engines in use elsewhere in the country. This is partly because there was little major industry in East Anglia and also because of the state of the roads at the time, which made the carriage of coal over any distance a slow and expensive business.

It is only where coal could be brought by boat or ship that steam engines were used to any extent. Thus the hinterland of Yarmouth and Lowestoft developed an

A sophisticated boiler in an industrial setting.

industry to support the large fishing fleets, and the towns of Ipswich and Norwich, both readily accessible by water, developed light industry. This centralisation of industry near the coalfields happened before the introduction of the railway network and the ability to move coal all round the country much more easily and cheaply. By the time the railways were effective, the precedent was set and the major industrial areas, by and large, did not stray far beyond their original locations.

Over this period improvements were introduced and steam engines became slightly more efficient as the designs improved. There were some early attempts at fitting automatic valves, but it was not until James Watt took the design forward that the

This wonderful rotative beam engine was built by Easton and Amos of Norwich.
Courtesy of the Kew Bridge Engines Trust

engines became significantly better. He realised that the most effective way to improve efficiency was to retain the heat in the working piston and to do this he designed a separate condenser, so that the action of condensation did not detract from the latent heat of the piston.

Watt's patents, which were to give him a virtual monopoly for twenty-five years from 1775, still applied to an engine that was driven by atmospheric pressure. However, he soon realised that the pressure of the steam itself was more powerful than the atmospheric pressure. Watt made use of the steam as well as the atmospheric pressure when he invented the reciprocating engine, utilising this double action. This was really the start of the supremacy of steam, for at last the engines were more powerful, efficient and economic. Furthermore, through a system of gears the power from the pistons was transferred to rotary movement.

Another Norwich-built pump showing scant regard for health and safety.

Although Watt had contributed major discoveries and innovations to the development of steam, the effect of his twenty-five-year patent was to hold back the overall development and it was not until the early 1800s, when the patent had expired, that the speed of development took off. The development of Watt's safety-valve principle, the use of higher pressures, improvements in boiler design to withstand the pressures, smaller and faster engines and the use of cranks rather than sun-and-planet gears, were all factors in bringing the steam engine into the factories and mills. In 1807 the table engine, patented by Henry Maudsley, and connected by belts to a line-shaft, became the forerunner of many factory and pithead applications.

Typical pumping-station engines from 1845 (foreground) and 1812, and the beams above.

As we have seen, the steam industry was initially developed in areas where there was a ready supply of coal and water, and the mills and factories tended to be concentrated in Lancashire and Yorkshire. The first extensive use of steam power in Norfolk was in drainage. Pumps that had been designed for pumping water out of coal mines were well suited to draining the fens. Until now this had been done by a large number of windmills, but they were unreliable, weather-dependent, and generally ineffective. Records show that in Littleport Fen just two steam engines were needed to drain an area of over 28 000 acres. Previously there had been 80 wind pumps, and these had not been able to cope with the task.

The requirement in land drainage is to raise comparatively large volumes of water through a small lifting height. The historic method of doing this was to use windmills to drive wheels with a number of small scoops.   A typical

Belt-driven sewage pumps at a sewage-treatment site.

Two ways of solving the mobile crane problem.

This lovely model of an early stationary engine can be seen in the Royal Scottish Museum. Stationary engines were put to many uses on the farm and in industry. Driving a line shaft in a pottery, powering generators, driving pumps, mills and all sorts of other machinery, they were a cheap and effective way of producing power. They could be towed around easily by a horse, or for short distances in a factory, could even be manhandled. Photograph by kind permission of the Royal Scottish Museum

scoop wheel might be 25 to 30 feet in diameter and have up to 40 scoops each about five feet wide and six feet long. This was an inefficient way to lift water because it required a heavy piece of equipment that was also expensive. Nevertheless, no one had come up with an alternative and it was the scoop wheel that continued in use even when steam power was introduced. A scoop wheel of the sort described driven at five rpm could lift over 300 tons of water a minute. It was not until 1850, and the introduction of the centrifugal pump, that the scoop system was progressively dropped.

At Sutton Marsh in Norfolk, in about 1862, a drainage engine constructed by Fletcher & Co. of Derby was installed to help drain the marsh. This was a simple beam engine of the Cornish type, which drove a scoop wheel to lift the water. It was usual for such engines to be put to use only when pumping was necessary, but this particular engine was dual-purpose, also driving a set of grinding stones for the production of flour. The engine remained in service until 1930, a testimony to the engineering skills of the early steam-engine producers.

In 1883 an Easton & Anderson engine was installed at Waldersea in Norfolk to drain an area of 5050 acres. This engine, typical of the Easton & Anderson engines of the time, was simplified in design. Simplicity and reliability were essential for such engines, which had to run for extended periods in their drainage role. The power was transferred to a toothed flywheel, ten feet in diameter, which in turn drove the vertical pump.

All these early engines were beam engines and they only achieved relatively low speeds, which is why they ran for so long without much maintenance. The Americans, led by George Corliss, developed a much faster engine capable of 100 rpm and this was quickly copied by British engineers. The new design could be applied to both vertical and horizontal engines but in general the horizontal design was preferred for industry. A further important development had been the 'compounding' of engines. This meant that the steam was used twice, once at very high pressure and then in a second cylinder at lower pressure. This made much more effective use of the potential power and helped to increase both speed and horse-power available.

A typical boiler shed for a small business.

In Norfolk and Suffolk, after drainage, an early application of steam power was in milling. Water mills, such as the famous mill at Pakenham in Suffolk, were fitted with auxiliary steam engines so that when the river was low and running slowly, the steam engine could be used to carry out the milling.

As electricity became more widely available and its use in industry started to spread, so steam engines were used to drive the dynamos that generated the electricity. In fact, it was for this purpose that the use of steam was retained long after it had disappeared from most other applications.

Gradually steam was introduced to industry across Norfolk and Suffolk, but while the counties remained essentially rural, the use of steam for industrial purposes was minimal. At Webbs Tannery at Coombs, Stowmarket, a single-cylinder grasshopper-design engine provided the power. At Newmarket, at the Southfields Pumping Station, an inverted triple-expansion vertical-pumping engine by Hawthorn & Davey was installed in 1910. At Lound pumping station at Lowestoft Waterworks there were two single-cylinder grasshopper engines built by Easton & Amos in about 1855.

Other types of industry employing steam included rope mills, waterworks, forges and potteries. A stationary steam engine from Henry Watson's Pottery at Wattisfield is

A steam generator set driven by a Bellis and Morcom triple-expansion steam engine.

A horizontal engine, originally used to drive belts and machinery in a jam factory and now preserved in working condition at Bressingham Steam Museum.

preserved at Bressingham. The Bridewell Museum in Norwich is also the resting place of a number of old engines including one from the Baggs Brewery in King's Lynn.

Although large and powerful machines were needed for the textile industry in the Midlands and the North of England, in Norfolk and Suffolk the requirement was generally for less powerful machines. A popular choice for factories was a side-by-side compound engine. In this type of design the two cylinders would be placed close together and a flywheel would be fitted to one side. These could produce up to 800 horsepower although the majority were below 350hp. A successful Norfolk manufacturer of such engines was Riches & Watts of Norwich. Their engines were supplied to many local businesses and one was working until very late on at the Young's Brewery in Norwich.

A further significant use of steam within industry was on the many works and light railways that served factories, docks and areas of mining and quarrying. The

Stationary industrial engines on display at Bressingham.

locomotives were usually saddle-tank engines, simply built, and often without any protection from the weather for the driver. Again, within Norfolk and Suffolk, and with the exception of some steam cranes at the docks, there were no significant industrial railways in the region. However, the British Sugar Corporation installed a railway at its Ipswich factory, where standard-gauge locomotives hauled sugar beet around the site. The locomotives came from a variety of sources. One, 'Beatrice', had been commandeered in the First World War to serve in a munitions depot at Aintree. After the war she was was bought by Handley Page at Cricklewood but was moved to Ipswich in 1925, where she continued to work until well into the 1950s.

Three locomotives from the Penryn Quarries can still be seen in operation at Bressingham Steam Museum, where there are also two locomotives from the Bekton works, and a dockside crane locomotive on static display.

Chapter Five

Railways

The story of rail development in Norfolk and Suffolk is something of a paradox. There was no apparent reason for early development of the railway into this backwater of England, comparatively untouched by the Industrial Revolution, and yet the railways made their first appearance surprisingly early. However, the completion of the network took a long time and many branch lines either never left the drawing-board or were only partially completed.

Norfolk and Suffolk had no major trading ports, there were no great centres of industry or population and therefore there was arguably no reason to invest in railway communications, the payback for which might never be achieved. Furthermore, many of the early schemes had backers who were not resident in the counties that the railways were to serve; their interest was purely financial.

As early as 1836 an Act was passed permitting the construction of a railway line from London to Colchester. The Eastern Counties Railway set about the task, with the original aim of stretching to Harwich, Ipswich and Norwich. By 1843 they had reached Colchester but the several years of investment had left the company short of cash and they were unable to fund any further development.

However, the story really starts almost twenty years before, back in 1824. It was the Norfolk & Suffolk Rail Road Company who first proposed to build a railway line from London, via Colchester and Ipswich to Norwich. There were to be branch lines to Harwich and Bury St Edmunds, and the total cost was then estimated at

A steam excavator being used to help construct the railway lines. Given the pioneering nature of the engineering and the relatively primitive nature of the tools, the construction of the rail network for Norfolk and Suffolk was a remarkable achievement. It was finance and not labour that impeded progress.

close to £1 million pounds with the company proposing to raise the capital by selling £100 shares.

In spite of an aggressive marketing campaign, sale of shares was slow. Potential investors were nervous about a comparatively new technology, doubtful that the line could be built for the stated cost and uncertain that it would ever be busy enough to return a profit. The result was that the capital could not be raised and the scheme was reduced in scope. In November 1825 it was announced by the directors that the new line would only go from Whitechapel to Ipswich and the company sought authority from Parliament to commence construction. All new railways required an Act of Parliament because in order to construct a line it was necessary to make compulsory purchase of the land over which the railway was to run.

In the event, the Norfolk & Suffolk Rail Road Company was unable to raise even the reduced amount of capital. There were scandals over the company trading illegally when it was technically bankrupt and there was further disquiet over the behaviour of an accountant, John Wilks. His books did not give an accurate record of the transactions of the company and Wilks himself, who later became Member of Parliament for Sudbury, appears to have raided the funds to support his habit of entertaining extravagantly.

A classic 2-4-0 locomotive with elegant lines but very little protection for the driver from the elements.

Meanwhile, in 1825 another embryo railway company, the Ipswich & Suffolk Railway, proposed the construction of a line from Ipswich to Eye and Diss. This also failed to get off the drawing-board, but was at least free from scandal and adverse publicity. Similarly, a further scheme in 1833 to link Bury St Edmunds, Hadleigh and Lavenham to Ipswich came to nothing.

By 1834 two railway companies were competing to build a line from London to York. The route for both railways was via Cambridge and both proposed a branch from Cambridge to Norwich. A year later the Eastern Counties Railway produced an ambitious and extravagant plan for a line from London to Ipswich.

Railway and locomotive engineering was in its infancy and gradients either had to be overcome by use of winding engines or by bringing the railway up to the highest level of the route and maintaining height. The Eastern Counties proposal therefore included some magnificent plans for vast viaducts.

The lobbying between the companies and the element of competition was fierce and on 4 July 1836 Parliament decided that the Northern & Eastern Railway should be granted a licence to build a line from London, but only as far as Cambridge, and the Eastern Counties Railway should be given authority to construct the line proposed from London to Yarmouth. Once this decision was made, others wanted to seize the opportunity and there were several plans to link with the Eastern Counties route, the main proposal being to revive the earlier scheme for a line from Bury St Edmunds to join the Eastern Counties line at Ipswich, or at Belstead to be exact.

The Eastern Counties Railway started construction in early 1837, working from the London end, but engineering difficulties in crossing the marshes and the Lea Valley, and a reluctance of shareholders to pay on call, meant that progress was very slow. By mid-1838 it was announced that for the time being the line would not be constructed beyond Colchester. This caused a rift amongst the directors, those from

An early industrial tank locomotive looking very much a cross between a railway engine and a traction engine!

Norfolk and Suffolk feeling particularly aggrieved having worked hard to negotiate the necessary compulsory land purchases in their counties.

With the boardroom bickering in the background and very slow progress on the ground itself – they had only reached Brentwood by July 1840 – those who were Norfolk-based opted to build an independent line from Norwich to Yarmouth.

A talented and experienced engineer, Peter Bruff, was employed by the Eastern Counties Railway, but they fell out over what Bruff considered to be a paltry remuneration for his skills. Bruff was probably right, he had the skills and was worth more than he was being paid, but the evidence was not there at the time and he was dismissed.

Bruff's reaction was to set about designing and finding backers for his own railway from Colchester to Ipswich and beyond. This was the birth of the Eastern Union Railway. Unlike the Eastern Counties Railway, the finance came almost exclusively from within the area that was to benefit from the railway and so there were many more vested interests in making it succeed. Furthermore, the breakaway group from the Eastern Counties Railway, planning the Norwich to Yarmouth line, clearly had a keen interest in seeing Bruff's plans completed and a line to Norwich constructed. The Eastern Union took up the challenge and by 1846 had extended the line to Ipswich.

An added complication in the early stages was the choice of rail gauge. The Eastern Counties Railway had wanted to adopt the seven-foot gauge of the Great Western but had been dissuaded by their chief engineer, and they had eventually settled on five-foot gauge. This in fact standardised the gauge within the region because the Northern & Eastern Railway, operating initially from Stratford to Bishops Stortford but planning to extend to Cambridge and there to link in with the planned Eastern Counties line, had also adopted five-foot gauge. As soon as it was realised that travel beyond Cambridge would be impossible without

Granville, a sturdy 0-4-0 tank locomotive now preserved in its original green livery at Bressingham. Built in 1893, it is a two-cylinder locomotive weighing almost 33½ tons. It spent much of its working life on Southampton Docks.

reduction to the standard gauge, the reduced gauge was adopted. Incredibly, the conversion took just a couple of months, with a service kept in being by the use of single-line running.

At the same time as the Eastern Union was pushing up to Ipswich, the line from London to Cambridge was completed, and then in 1845 further extended to link in with the Norwich & Brandon. This provided a through-route from London to Norwich.

At this time there was a plethora of small railway companies; mergers and takeovers were regular events. Most went the way of the Eastern Counties Railway. The Norwich & Brandon, along with the Yarmouth & Norwich, formed the Norfolk Railway, and this was taken over in 1846 by the Eastern Counties. (Incidentally, the British rail-speed record for a mile in forty-four seconds was held by the Yarmouth & Norwich line for quite a few years!) The East Anglian Railway was based on two centres, at King's Lynn and Ely, and they were also subsumed in 1852. The Eastern Union, having completed the Colchester to Ipswich link, was taken over in 1854 and the East Suffolk, operating to Yarmouth and Lowestoft, was taken over in 1859. Eventually, in 1862, the various companies were brought together to form the Great Eastern Railway. For obvious reasons the railway was affectionately known as 'The Swedey'!

This rather scruffy looking steam crane is typical of the type of useful construction 'plant' for the early railways. With a compact, vertical boiler, it was easy to fire up and economical to run. It was self-mobile, through a simple system of gears to the axles, and the crane, with its long jib, was ideal for lifting sections of rail into place.

Financial scandals are not just a feature of the present age and the Eastern Counties Railway went through its own major scandal. In common with almost all the railways in Norfolk and Suffolk, the company found it difficult to make ends meet. None of the railways was a great financial success, but the Eastern Counties found it more difficult than many. George Hudson had taken over as chairman in 1845 but instead of declaring financial difficulties at the time, the company continued to pay out share dividends by robbing the company's capital. The inevitable happened and the company crashed in 1848. Creditors made angry protest and even stormed Shoreditch Station and seized carriages to compensate for money owed.

The company managed to survive and continued to operate, but improvement and all but essential maintenance were unaffordable. It became the laughing-stock of the railway world at the time. This sorry state of affairs lasted until the Great Eastern Railway came under the chairmanship of Lord Cranborne, Marquess of Salisbury. Together with an honest and very competent team he restored the reputation and to some extent the fortunes of the Great Eastern Railway.

The link with London took on its present-day form with the opening of Liverpool Street Station as the Great Eastern Railway London terminus in 1875. The terminal served both lines from London to Norwich via Cambridge and Ely, and via Colchester and Ipswich.

South of Suffolk, the port of Harwich was also being developed and the new Parkeston Quay was completed in 1882. The quay was named after Parkes who had succeeded Lord Salisbury as chairman of the Great Eastern Railway. He was renowned for his thoroughness and diligence and the railway continued to prosper under his leadership. By 1893, the modern facility at Harwich helped to win for

Above: *Tank engines, such as these robust 2-6-4 4 MT mixed-traffic locomotives, were the work-horses of the branch lines and the suburban and local traffic. They were introduced in 1934 and this particular locomotive was in service with the LMS originally. It was one of a batch of three-cylinder variants specifically designed for providing greater acceleration. No. 42500 was based at Shoeburyness.*

Right: *Because most pictures of steam locomotives are taken from a distance, it is easy to overlook their sheer size. It is interesting to compare the height of these museum visitors with the driving wheels of the locomotive.*

Left: *To speed up the collection and delivery of mail, this simple, but ingenious system of bags, hooks and nets was used. Mail was sorted into very robust leather satchels and these were suspended from hooks and swept up by a cradle arrangement on the side of the collecting wagon. At the same time, a simple trip device deposited the mail to be delivered into the net below.*

Below: *Simple and functional tank engines such as this 0-4-0 were used in the rail-served factories and also to support track building and maintenance, where the movement of rail was a considerable task.*

Early morning steam in the depot at Shoeburyness.

the port the all-important mail contract to the Continent. This channelled rail traffic from the North and the Midlands through Suffolk and Haughley Junction to Harwich.

A problem peculiar to Norfolk, with its low-lying broadland landscape, was that the main line and several branch lines had to cross the many waterways of the county. There were few natural hills and so the railway engineers had to come up with the riverine answer to the level crossing – the swing-bridge. Ingenious though they were, such bridges imposed speed restrictions and delays either for the trains or for the many sea-going ships that still used the navigable waterways now restricted by the presence of the bridges. Swing-bridges or their remains can still be seen at Trowse, Reedham, Somerleyton, Carlton Colville, St Olaves, Beccles and Brightlingsea.

Although the famed flatness of the landscape presented the railway engineers with no major problems, there were other interesting obstacles to overcome. Early on, the crossing of the marshes to Stratford had seen the first use of steam pile-drivers in this country, required to put the necessary foundations in place. The gentle, rolling nature of the countryside in some areas provided several testing gradients. In Norfolk and Suffolk there are fast-flowing rivers that have carved out wide valleys and extensive flood plains and so the railway had to cope with these undulations.

By 1882 Great Eastern Railway had joined forces with the Great Northern to build the line from Ely to Doncaster. Ten years later this was to be extended to York and the 'Cathedrals Line' was established linking York with Lincoln and Ely. This all helped in the concentration of rail and, in particular, mail traffic to Harwich and the Continent. It also meant that there were excellent rail services available to the Norfolk coast and to Newmarket for the racing. The Royal family started using trains to travel to Sandringham (Wolferton Station) and the large fishing fleets of Lowestoft and Yarmouth were able to serve the London markets thanks to a speedy service straight into the East End.

In Lord Claud Hamilton, the Great Eastern Railway found a leader who was able to combine the financial management of Lord Salisbury with the attention to detail and railway-operating skills of Parkes. His General Manager, William Birt (later Sir William Birt) supported him ably and they were a formidable team that really established the Great Eastern Railway.

A feature of rail travel of that age was the use of slip coaches. Coaches and wagons from other railways would be attached to the train of a neighbouring railway, or beyond, to take goods, mail and passengers through to their destination. An observer at Haughley Junction would certainly have seen coaches from almost every major railway in Britain on their way to or from the Continent.

2-4-0 No. 62785 E4 Class locomotive (GER 490) hauling a local train. The E4 was a common sight on the railways of Norfolk and Suffolk. The two-cylinder engine was designed by James Holden and this locomotive was built in Stratford in 1895. It made no claim to speed but was designed to tackle the cross-country routes and slow, main-line duties. The locomotive weighed just over 40 tons and had a working boiler pressure of 160lbs psi. No. 490 remained in service for a remarkable sixty-four years and was withdrawn, when still in good working order, in 1959. (It is now preserved at Bressingham, on loan from the National Railway Museum.)

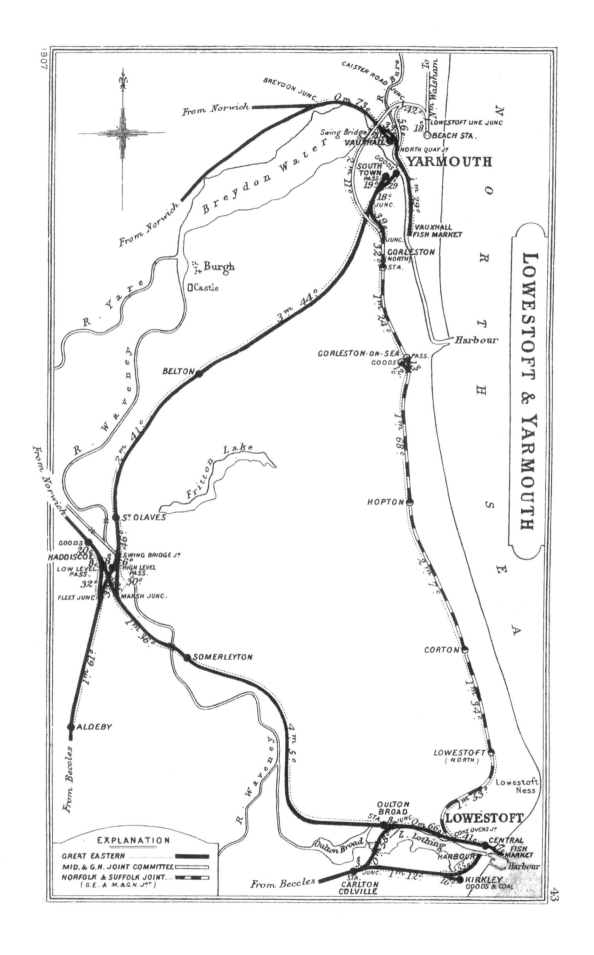

LOWESTOFT & YARMOUTH

EXPLANATION

GREAT EASTERN _____
MID. & G.N. JOINT COMMITTEE _____
NORFOLK & SUFFOLK JOINT _____
(G.E. & M.& G.N. J⁹ᵗ)

The Great Eastern Railway also started to enjoy a wonderful reputation for service, reliability and punctuality. As it neared London it served the rapidly expanding commuter population of Essex; the railway carried more passengers than any other in the country.

To support what was a busy railway, the engineering works were mostly centralised at Stratford. Originally the Eastern Union had its works at Ipswich and the Norfolk Railway had works at Norwich, but these were small organisations and the amalgamation into the Great Eastern Railway brought the centralisation based on East London.

Because of the number of different railway companies that had been amalgamated, and for a variety of reasons thereafter, the Great Eastern Railway started life with a remarkable variety of locomotives. In 1885 the company appointed James Holden as Locomotive Superintendent. He served for twenty-three years, eventually handing over to his son. He had come from the Great Western and was appalled at the variety of equipment, rolling-stock and fittings and set about simplification and standardisation. He also set high standards for maintenance and cleanliness of the locomotives, engendering that feeling of pride that drivers have when they are in charge of a well-turned-out locomotive.

Driver Harry Plum preparing for the day's work with this 2-6-4 4 MT standard tank locomotive. No. 80103 was designed and built at Brighton as part of a series of the British Railways' standard locomotive programme. The locomotive worked from the region into London, Fenchurch Street.

In 1900 he introduced the 'Claud Hamilton', a 4-4-0 locomotive and one of the finest looking ever to be seen on Britain's railways. A few years later, Mr Hill, successor to James Holden's son, introduced a 4-6-0 variant of the Claud Hamilton and with these two locomotives as the mainstay of their fleet, the Great Eastern Railway had locomotive power that stood comparison with any. Hill also introduced a series of 0-6-0 shunting engines, which were the most powerful and reliable in the country.

The coming of the railways had a profound effect on society – it was not just the opening up of new markets and the availability of travel but, of course, the railways offered a source of permanent employment. They needed drivers, firemen, signalmen, stationmasters and station staff, clerks, porters, tracklayers and maintenance teams, workshop staff and a whole management structure to control and run the operation as a proper business.

A less obvious effect was that the railways changed the diet of the nation. From quite an early stage in the life of steamships, refrigeration was possible and frozen meats came in from Australia and South America, and wheat came from the Americas. Fruit arrived from the tropics, dairy produce and bacon from Denmark, cheese from France, and from the New World, nuts, sultanas, raisins, and so forth. Even animal feed and hay to feed the still-numerous horses of Norfolk and Suffolk were brought in by ship. All these goods were then transported by the railways. Before rail transport it had been quite possible to bring these items to Britain but almost impossible to move any quantities beyond the immediate hinterland of the arrival port. Now such produce could be moved rapidly around the country and diets changed as a result.

The need to produce accurate timetables and to be able to tell potential passengers when the train would arrive and depart led to the standardisation of time across Britain. The initiative for this came not from East Anglia but from the West Country. The problem was that each town worked on the true time of day, thus Reading was four minutes later than London time, Cirencester was another three-and-a-half minutes later and Bridgewater fourteen minutes behind London. Norwich was three minutes ahead of London. Clearly, this made producing a timetable quite a complicated process! The answer was to introduce London Time to all parts of Britain and Ireland. The problem was how to let everyone know what the time was. It was the railway, which needed the standardisation, which also provided the tool for achieving it. The mail coaches would carry clocks set to London or, more accurately, Greenwich Mean Time, and station and town clocks along the route would be synchronised on a daily basis. Exactly the same principle was used to carry the time to Ireland, with the time being 'handed over' at Holyhead and then taken across to Dublin.

An early leisure use of the railways developed very quickly after the establishment of the line from London. In the mid-1800s boxing had not been established as an official sport and its predecessor, prize fighting, was illegal. The attentions of the police had all but stopped prize fighting in London and so the activity moved to quieter locations. The idea was that the spectators would be carried by train to some

Preparing the mail.

remote spot that was inaccessible by other means. Here the fight would be staged, money would change hands and the train return everyone home before the police caught up with events. One of the earliest recorded such fights took place at Six-Mile Bottom on the Suffolk–Cambridge border in October 1840. The police tried to intervene but were fed false information and diverted elsewhere in Suffolk.

Although illegal, this was a profitable business and the Eastern Counties Railways took the view that if passengers wanted to travel, it was not the business of the railway company to question their motives. Special trains were organised to carry substantial crowds of up to 500 to prize-fight venues.

Other, less dubious, leisure traffic also grew. Excursions to the Norfolk coast were popular from the mid-1840s onwards and special trains were organised to carry passengers from both within and from outside the region, to Yarmouth in particular. Excursions also went the other way, to London, especially if there was a special event. The Great Exhibition of 1851 was one such entertainment and the railway company made a handsome profit running many thousands of visitors to the exhibition.

Some excursions were organised by outside groups or companies and by the 1850s an embryo Thomas Cook organisation was advertising excursions all over Britain, booking trains, accommodation and activities, and creating the first railway package tours.

Excursions became enormously popular. They were relatively cheap and, for the passenger, a reasonable degree of comfort was provided, albeit the day-trip could be a very long affair, starting early in the morning and returning late at night. For the railway company, it was good business. Holidays for the working classes were few and far between and once an excursion was booked there was little scope on the part of the customer to change the dates. If the weather turned poor, then that was the luck of the draw – you still went to Yarmouth and got cold! In their book *The Life and Times of the Great Eastern Railway*, Paar and Gray cite a Whit Monday excursion from Cambridge to London, which had to be split into several trains because there were bookings for passengers sufficient to fill 77 carriages!

As excursions grew in popularity, some firms started using them as a way to provide group holidays for their workers. Sometimes these were relatively small affairs, but on other occasions it became a major logistical operation with up to 10 000 workers and their families being moved from the Midlands to the Norfolk coast and back for a single day out. One recorded visit shows that the brewers, Bass & Co., needed 230 carriages to bring their party from Burton-on-Trent to Yarmouth, with trains leaving Burton every ten minutes from 3.45am to 6.00am.

Sport also generated a considerable amount of traffic with football in particular attracting large crowds from Norfolk and Suffolk to see the big names in and around London. Horse-racing at Yarmouth and Newmarket, although on a less regular basis, still brought a need for special trains. At Newmarket major investment was made in the station and its infrastructure; the traffic could be considerable with over 7500 passengers arriving by train for a race meeting. Horse-racing also required its own support and the movement of horses to different meetings around the country became much easier by train.

Rail travel reached a high degree of comfort, especially for the first-class passenger.

Horse-racing was very much the sport of the wealthy and it was really only on the Newmarket run that the Great Eastern Railway entered the luxury travel business. They did it so well that Newmarket Station benefited greatly from a donation given to the railway company by the wealthy Colonel McCalmont, as an expression of his appreciation!

Tourism was treated seriously by the railways and considerable expenditure went into promoting the delights offered in East Anglia. On 17 May 1912, a special train was arranged to take a large party of London and Provincial press representatives to Aldeburgh, thus demonstrating the facility that the railway offered and promoting the attraction of this once busy port and the neighbouring district. In the afternoon they travelled by coach via Yoxford, to Southwold where they stayed at the Grand Hotel. On the next day, the Saturday, they were taken by coach to Halesworth, where a restaurant car picked them up and returned them to London. It was a journey remarkably similar to that undertaken by the Guild of Travel Writers, as guests of the East of England Tourist Board, ninety years later! The literature at the time announced that 'This season a full summer train service will commence to run on 1 July. Seven trains daily will run between Liverpool Street and Aldeburgh in each direction and there will be six trains to, and five from, Southwold. Three of the Aldeburgh trains will have restaurant cars and two of the Southwold trains.'

After the poor record of its earlier days, the Great Eastern Railway built up an impressive record for efficiency and punctuality – a fact that it was always ready to share with its customers. One notice informed passengers that on Saturday 12 October 1901, 'all the business trains (8–11am) arrived at the Liverpool Street terminus on time with the exception of one, which was two minutes late. This of course means that the departures were also correspondingly exact, and as some 160 trains were concerned, it probably represents a record for our chief London Suburban Railway.' Considering the volume of traffic at the time this was a pretty remarkable achievement.

Passengers started to enjoy considerable comfort and by 1897 the Great Eastern Railway was running dining cars on their trains between York and Harwich and these were 'much appreciated by the travelling public'. Passengers could, however, cause problems and there were always a few who wished to bend the rules. One such is described in this splendid caricature from the *Railway Magazine* of June 1897:

The Old Lady Passenger

To the station there came an elderly dame
Some hours before the train started,
And she'd luggage galore and boxes a score
From which she declined to be parted.
And the platform she paced and she wished they'd make haste,
As she had to travel some distance;
And she pursed up her lips and declined to give tips
To the porters who offered assistance.

When at length the train came, that elderly dame
Got into a carriage marked 'first',
And the guard she sought to ask if he thought
The engine or boiler would burst;
And the guard got riled, and his language was wild
And loudly the door he did slam,
So no more did she ask, but took out a flask,
And treated herself to a dram.

Whene'er the train stopped, from the window there popped
The head of that elderly dame,
And she loudly did try, from each passer-by,
To ask of that station the name.
But each passer-by from that lady did fly,
And so she got no satisfaction,
And she hailed every porter, till crazy they thought her,
And drove the whole lot to distraction.

With her luggage galore, and boxes a score,
She filled up the seats on each side;

And under the seat, concealed by her feet
A little blue spaniel did ride.
But, sad to remark, that spaniel did bark,
Just when the inspector came round,
For the dog was not booked, and vainly she looked
For a ticket that could not be found.

So she tried to explain, but, alas all in vain,
And she tried the inspector to square,
But his chief was in sight, or he otherwise might
Have contented himself with the fare.
So that elderly dame had to give up her name,
And write on a card her address,
And they weighed up her kit, and she'd almost a fit
When she heard the amount of excess.

In less than a week a neighbouring beak
For that elderly lady did send,
And he said 'twas a shame that an elderly dame
Should herself to such practices lend.
But if elderly dames tried such queer little games,
They surely would get into trouble;
So he sent her away – forty shillings to pay,
And costs which amounted to double.

In those days, around the end of the nineteenth century, Liverpool Street Station of the Great Eastern Railway was the busiest commuter terminus in London. It was almost self-induced for the railway ran virtually twenty-four hours a day carrying workers, the mail, newspapers and goods to and from the markets of London. Because the service existed, more and more people moved to the north-eastern outskirts where they could buy a suburban house, out of the city itself, and still get to and from work. Records show that on Tuesday 18 October 1898, 67 210 passengers arrived at the station and 69 335 departed. It was a round-the-clock service. The timetable began at 1.00am but the trains ran continuously throughout the twenty-four hours, with the only gap being for a couple of hours on a Sunday morning. A contributor to the *Railway Magazine* wrote of how he overheard at the barrier to Platform 3 late one evening, the following exchange:

'Porter, what time does the last train go to Walthamstow?'

'Lor' bless you marm, there ain't no last train to Walthamstow.'

In those days there was no problem in getting a late train back after the theatre or the opera! But it was not just the commuter trains; 3am saw the arrival of the mail train from Yarmouth, Lowestoft, Cromer and Norwich, and a little stream of heavy-eyed passengers could usually be seen ascending the stairs to the station hotel.

The evening mail trains to the Continent left at 8.30pm for the Hook of Holland boat and at 8.40pm for the Antwerp boat.

It is also worth mentioning the arrival of the two Continental expresses, one from Antwerp arrived at 7.35 in the morning and that from the Hook at 8.10am. As a contemporary commentator remarked:

> *... the scene during the customs examination is an animated one; there is much hand-shaking and kissing among old friends long parted, and the embracing is not confined to the sterner sex; bearded foreigners hug and kiss one another with an apparent appreciation of the odour of cheap tobacco and garlic. Similar in some respects to the foregoing, and yet in direct contrast, is the scene enacted when the P&O special leaves Liverpool Street for Tilbury. Then we stay-at-homes may obtain some faint, far-away notion of what our Indian Empire is. There are middle-aged sunburnt officers and liver-cursed civilians going back to their duties; young subalterns about to join their regiments, saying farewell to fond mothers and sisters; wives and children going back to join husbands and fathers; calm, impassive Orientals, fez-topped or turban crowned, and brightly attired ayahs, crooning some old world heathen lullaby to the young Christians in their charge.*

Oliver Cromwell and Thundersley arriving at Diss on their own wheels, but hauled by diesel. Both locomotives are owned by the NRM and are on display at Bressingham.

At 11.22pm the restaurant train arrived from Cromer, followed ten minutes later by that from Yarmouth. On Mondays two restaurant trains preceded these at 9.41pm and 10.45pm from Clacton and Cromer respectively. The success and popularity of these trains carrying first- and third-class restaurant cars was clear. Instead of an early, hurried and unsatisfactory meal at the seaside, passengers now breakfasted at ease en route.

Equally appreciated was the table d'hote dinner served on the 4.55pm and 5.00pm trains to Cromer and Yarmouth respectively. On Saturdays luncheon was served on the 1.30pm express to Cromer. This train was the most popular one to Cromer throughout the summer. It stopped only at North Walsham, for the convenience of Mundersley passengers, and so covered the journey to Cromer in two hours and fifty-five minutes. During the winter months it stopped at Ipswich and Norwich, and of course took a little longer on the journey. In fact in 1897 the Cromer Express was timetabled to complete the journey non-stop from Liverpool Street to North Walsham (130.75 miles) in two hours forty-five minutes. This was a challenging target but over the whole season it averaged just two minutes late – a record that Anglia Railways might well be proud of today.

Many of those going on holiday or away for a short break also liked to take another relatively new and popular innovation with them – their bicycles. Ticket records at Liverpool Street show that 1300 bicycles booked on a single day on trains to Norfolk and Suffolk was quite normal. Even in those days, this was 'England's Cycling Country'.

The reliability and accessibility of the railway to the Norfolk and Suffolk coast made it very popular. It was practical to take day-trips, or to use the excellent-value tourist tickets, that allowed passengers to break their journey and make a number of stops. This made it an attractive destination for touring and cycling holidays. Reporting on the day after a bank holiday, the *Daily Telegraph* of 8 August 1899 reported that:

> *... at Liverpool Street is to be seen the most impressive illustration of the vast efflux from London. Let the man who has never witnessed it go down on a bank holiday morning to the iron footbridge that spans its score or so of platforms, and he will never forget the spectacle. Below is a crowd which must at any time of the day run into thousands, flowing in obedience to ubiquitous placards and direction boards towards the various starting points, while the stout bridge itself vibrates and sways under the ceaseless stream which flows over it.*

According to the *Railway Magazine* this was an accurate description, for on that day 40 000 tickets were sold at Liverpool Street Station. Of course there were many more who had return tickets or who had bought their tickets in advance. Furthermore, the traffic was not all one-way 'for just as the tired cockney hies him forth to the country or the seaside upon a bank holiday, so his country cousins come in goodly numbers to the great metropolis.'

Nothing succeeds like success. The skills and leadership of the manager, William Birt, were recognised and he was highly respected by his staff. In 1897 he was knighted for services to the railway and his grateful staff organised a subscription to buy a present to mark the event. They collected sufficient to buy a large canteen of solid silver cutlery for Sir William, and for Lady Birt they bought a grand piano and a diamond brooch.

The company was progressive and responsive. It met the needs of the local and rural communities. Goods and agricultural traffic was important and in 1897 the records show that 30 074 tons of potatoes, 2553 tons of carrots, 5691 tons of cattle feed, 12 544 tons of vegetables and 1162 tons of fruit were carried. These volumes are reflected in the quantities of rolling-stock held at the time. By 1899, in addition to the locomotives and passenger coaches, the company owned 452 horseboxes, 55 cattle wagons, 186 goods trucks, 355 brake vans, 23 milk vans, 124 fish vans, 110 sundry vans, 11 tramcars, 32 omnibuses and 1 invalid carriage. In the same year they attracted considerable criticism because they decided to build 50 new locomotives, at a cost of £85 000, out of capital. Until then locomotives had been built from revenue and investors were concerned that the railway was reverting to the lack of control that had been displayed forty years previously. They had no cause to worry, for the company was in sound hands and the investment was to help keep the Great Eastern Railway at the forefront of the railway services in England. An important factor was the customer-oriented view that the company always seemed to take and, ahead of its time, it always tried to introduce more facilities and comfort for its passengers. Thus, in the same year they also began a programme of fitting lavatories to all first-class carriages, and to 70 of the third-class coaches. They also introduced four new dining cars and 30 more modern passenger wagons.

In spite of this laudable attitude, they still had the odd brush with their passengers and in 1899 it was complained that 'when trains arrive at the termini filled with passengers, the porters do not attempt to open the doors unless they see passengers with luggage from whom they expect tips. This is a small matter when inside handles are provided, but far from every carriage is as yet so fitted and during wet, damp or foggy weather the outside handles are very unpleasant to touch, and cannot be handled without injury to the gloves of the wearers.' The case went to court and the judge agreed with the passengers and ruled that porters were provided for such purposes. He awarded damages against the railway for negligence!

2-6-4 tank No. 89072 setting out to find work.

Although rather off the beaten track, the railways of Norfolk and Suffolk played a variety of roles in the First World War. Bathhouses were set up at Newmarket and elsewhere so that soldiers in transit could wash. Ambulance trains helped to disperse incoming casualties from the ports to the hospitals around the region, and prisoners of war were moved in the same way. In some cases the increase in traffic became so much that additional temporary signalling systems and boxes had to be introduced.

The threat of sabotage to the railways was realised and military guards were mounted on key installations, bridges and viaducts. However, one aspect that was overlooked originally was that the railways were very convenient signposts because they pointed to the main concentrations of industry and population, and German navigators found them useful tools to help guide them to their targets. Even at night, with black-out restrictions in force, the railways could easily be picked out by airship pilots. It was one such airship that followed the railway line to King's Lynn and then released its bombs. Considerable damage was done but fortunately no one was killed on this occasion and the papers were able to jest about renaming the town 'Zeppe-Lynn'!

The staff of the railways were an organised body with reasonably advanced communications for the time and so the railway set up a monitoring and reporting system to give warning and information about incoming Zeppelins.

In both this conflict and the Second World War, the loss of the sea crossing from Harwich had a considerable effect on the railway. In the First World War the railway company also owned many of the ships and these were converted to troop-carrying

The narrow-guage branch at Southwold, April 1929.

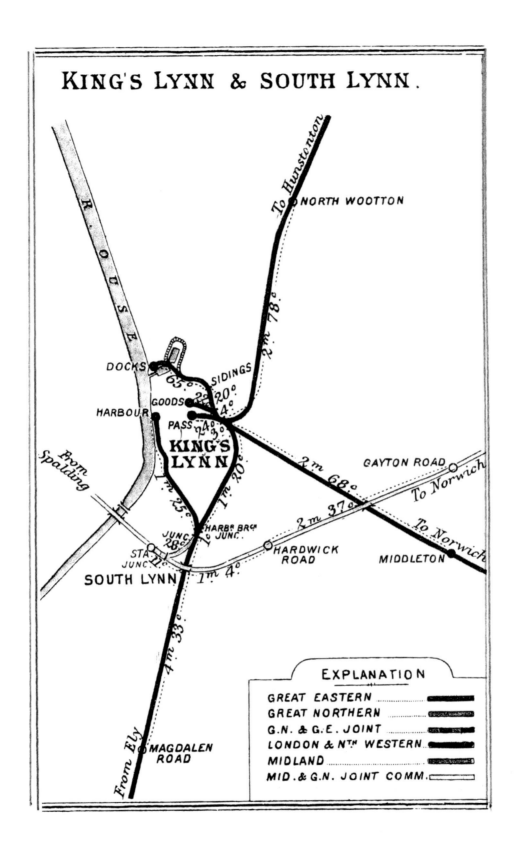

KING'S LYNN & SOUTH LYNN.

duties, while in the Second World War traffic to re-supply airfields and depots replaced the much-diminished mail traffic.

Norfolk and Suffolk did not escape the 'Beeching Axe' and a map of the railways sixty years ago shows a very different picture from that of today. In south Suffolk a line from Bentley to Hadleigh joined the Ipswich to Colchester main line at Bentley. From Colchester it was possible to take the train to Sudbury, Long Melford, Lavenham and Bury St Edmunds. Branches off the Ipswich–Lowestoft line led to Wickham Market, Snape, Aldeburgh, Framlingham and Southwold. From the Ipswich to Norwich Line it was possible to change for Laxfield at the end of the Mid-Suffolk Line (which ended in a field – it was supposed to link up with the Halesworth to Southwold line thus providing a link via Bury St Edmunds for the Midlands to the Suffolk coast, but it was never finished). Further branches led to Eye; Scole; Harleston, Bungay and Beccles; Wymondham, Dereham and either Swaffham, Narborough, King's Lynn, or County School, Fakenham, Walsingham and Wells.

A line along the Norfolk coast threaded its way from Lowestoft to Yarmouth, and then via Haddiscoe, where it joined the line from Beccles and on to North Walsham, Hundesley on Sea, Cromer and Sheringham. It then followed today's North Norfolk Railway to Holt and then to Wells, Hunstanton, Heacham, and Wolferton (for Sandringham) and King's Lynn.

From King's Lynn lines radiated out across the Fens to Spalding, Wisbech and Peterborough, Denver and Stoke Ferry, Narborough, Swaffham and Fakenham. The Swaffham line carried on via Thetford to Bury St Edmunds and there were several links into Cambridgeshire, Huntingdonshire and Lincolnshire. In central and north Norfolk another web of lines linked Wroxham, Aylsham, Melton Constable, Fakenham, County School and Dereham.

There were at least 44 of these branch lines and it is hardly surprising that it was uneconomical to run them all, but one cannot but wonder how much less congested the A11, A12, A14 and A140 might be today if these lines were still operating.

A goods train at Stoke by Clare, 1865.

GER 0-4-4 Johnson tank locomotive 186. No. 189 was to crash at Lavenham Bank in 1891. (See chapter 8.)

In addition, several other lines were planned in considerable detail but never found the backing to carry the plans forward to construction.

Branch lines were built for various purposes – to support a particular industry, to link market towns to the main line, to facilitate the movement of farm produce and so forth. There is not the space in this study to cover each line but the Mid-Suffolk Light Railway, the 'Middy', has been taken as an example, to give the flavour of work and routine on a branch line.

Like many of the branch lines in Norfolk and Suffolk, the 'Middy' was built at the turn of the century to serve the villages and agriculture of the region. Haughley Junction Station was enlarged in 1903 to cope with the additional role as terminus for the line. It was never envisaged that the 'Middy' would carry heavy locomotives and traffic and so the line was built to light standards to Mendlesham, Brockford, Kenton, Aspall and Laxfield. The railway opened in 1904 and was later extended as far as Cratfield for freight only. The original plan was to create a link across to Southwold to provide a rail link from the Midlands through to the Suffolk coast. It was also planned to create a further link with the East Suffolk Railway, which ran via Debenham and Otley to Ipswich, but these links were never built.

The Mid-Suffolk wanted to share the station facility at Haughley Junction and approached the Great Eastern Railway to ask them to arrange the necessary

An ex-LMS 2-6-0 4 MT mixed-traffic locomotive introduced in 1947. These locomotives became the standard design for British Railways locomotives. This locomotive was 'shedded' at Melton Constable in Norfolk for working the principal passenger trains on the Midland & Great Northern Joint Line, notably the services between Great Yarmouth/Lowestoft and Leicester.

enlargement. The Great Eastern Railway quoted such an enormous sum that the 'Middy' took fright and they decided to build their own station adjacent to the existing Haughley Junction Station. In the official records the two stations are shown as Haughley East for the 'Middy' and Haughley West for the Great Eastern Railway, but in practice the locals grouped the two together and continued to call them Haughley Junction. The new station was skilfully built to give the impression of a substantial station but it was actually a timber frame covered with zinc sheets and then well painted. It might almost have been the prototype for the old Hornby tin-plate model station!

Sadly, and again like many of the branch lines, it was difficult to make ends meet. The extension to Cratfield closed after just six years. The cattle docks that had been provided at every station were never properly used and they fell into disrepair and were soon scrapped as corn started to replace cattle as the main agricultural focus. A start had been made on the link to Kenton and Debenham but as raw materials became scarce in the First World War, it was decided to lift the part of the line that had been laid because the materials were wanted for more important purposes. This effectively destroyed any plans for completing the original scheme.

The 'Middy' stumbled along but was never a profitable affair. In 1924 it was officially taken over, along with the Great Eastern Railway, by the London & North Eastern Railway (LNER) but the LNER showed no interest in this backwater and the 'Middy' continued to operate virtually independently. The only change on which the LNER insisted was the closure of the 'Middy' terminus, Haughley East, and centralisation on the old Great Eastern Railway station. The 'Middy' terminus was flattened.

From a driver's point of view, the 'Middy' also presented a few challenges. The line out of Haughley was up an exacting 1-in-43 gradient and with no run at the slope, it was a good test of both locomotive and driver. However, it was the return journey on which more problems occurred. A 'runaway' train coming down the gradient could never have stopped and there was always the risk that a train might crash through the terminus at Haughley and on to the main line. There are several recorded incidents of trains overshooting at Haughley but fortunately none was serious. To try to minimise the risk strict weight limits were applied and whilst the up-trains were allowed to haul 21 wagons, the down-trains were limited to 14.

At first the 'Middy' provided a part-time service running on just three days a week for both passengers and freight. This was increased to a daily train in the sugar-beet season and the trains were usually mixed passenger and freight. In 1920 a daily passenger service was introduced, largely to carry schoolchildren, and at its peak four trains were run each way for six days a week with just one train each way on Sundays.

The 'Middy' and most of the other branch lines never really grew up in terms of operating infrastructure and there was an unmistakable air of self-help and improvisation about these little railways. The 'Middy' had just two signals on the entire line and these were at Haughley. The level-crossing gates, of which there were several between Haughley and Laxfield, were all opened and closed by the train crew themselves. The timetable was flexible with an estimated travelling time between sixty-four and seventy-five minutes to complete a journey along the full length of the line.

The 'Middy' had a slight resurgence in the Second World War when it was used to move munitions and supplies for some of the Suffolk air bases but after the war use dwindled. It survived the 1948 nationalisation, but only just, and in 1952 it was closed. Nature and agriculture between them quickly reclaimed the track bed and within a few years it was almost impossible to trace the route of the railway. A keen map-reader and observer might still be able to find a few traces here and there but even along the 'Middy' footpath, it is difficult to imagine that trains once ran along the same route.

An ex-LMS 4 F mixed traffic locomotive. No. 44581 was introduced in 1924 and was based at Cricklewood. It was predominantly a freight locomotive used for coal traffic between the Midlands and London but they were used to haul summer Saturday passenger holiday trains from the Midlands to East Anglia.

A preservation society has now been established, based at Brockford. The original station building from Brockford was recovered from a garden in Old Newton and has now been restored. A short length of track has been re-laid and some demonstration steam operations are carried out. The station buildings from Horham and Laxfield are preserved at Mangapps Farm Railway in Essex.

The disappearance of the branch lines and the loss of much of the interconnecting rail network that was woven across the counties had different effects in different places. To take an example from each county – Melton Constable in Norfolk and Haughley in Suffolk – both played significant and key roles in the hey-day of steam railways. The loss of role as the network shrank and modern motive power replaced steam affected these two places in totally different ways.

Melton Constable was linked to King's Lynn by the Lynn and Fakenham Railway in 1882 and then in 1887 the village was linked to Cromer. The village was quickly developed as a railway junction and as a railway works. There was little available local labour and so cheap housing was built to attract workers to the area and the railway company paid the rents for those who moved in. In contrast to the housing, the works' buildings were substantial structures and expected to serve for many years. Remnants of them can still be seen today, complete with the scars of bombing raids in the Second World War. Thus a railway community was created from nothing, really as a result of an accident of location, and the village grew out of all proportion to its neighbours as a key railway centre.

Saddle-tank locomotive Becket *at Ipswich.*

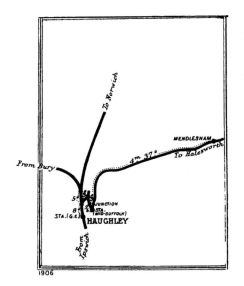

Along with other Beeching casualties, and in spite of a determined effort to continue when all around was closing, the line from Melton Constable to Sheringham eventually closed in April 1962. The railway workers had dispersed over a number of years in search of other employment and the village, whilst it will never return to its character of pre-railway days, has slipped back into something of a backwater. The traces of busier times are there but there is a strange, almost ghost-town feel to the place.

Haughley had been a thriving small market settlement in the sixteenth and seventeenth centuries. It was well placed for communications, sitting astride routes from Ipswich to Bury St Edmunds and from Colchester to Thetford and Lynn. It had its own docks at Dagworth and it was just a couple of miles to Stowmarket and then via Bramford to Ipswich. When the Ipswich & Bury Railway Company built a line from Ipswich, first to Stowmarket (July 1845) and then to Bury (1846), Haughley Station was built within easy walking distance of the village centre. Haughley had a direct link with London via Ipswich and Colchester. If this had been the end of the story perhaps Haughley would have prospered and grown, but the local saying is that Stowmarket grew from the ruins of Haughley, and it was the coming of the railway that was a key factor.

In early 1847, when the Ipswich & Bury Railway merged with the Eastern Union Railway, they started to build the line from Ipswich to Norwich. The first stretch to Haughley already existed but here they divided the line and headed north to Finningham by 1848, Burston in July 1849 and finally to Norwich Victoria Station (later to Thorpe Station) on 7 November 1849.

The first timetables show that the journey time from London to Ipswich was eighty minutes, to Haughley in ninety-four minutes and to Norwich in two hours and twelve minutes. Considering the far greater number of stops in those days, the journey times remain remarkably good in comparison with those of today! Indeed in recent months there is many a commuter who would have settled for a journey time of ninety-four minutes from Haughley to London!

The problem for Haughley was that the original station, convenient for the village, was the wrong side of the new Haughley Junction. It clearly would have been nonsense to have to go to Stowmarket and change trains if you wanted to go to Norwich, and so a new station that could serve both the Norwich and the Bury routes was constructed at the junction. The original station was dismantled after a short working life of just three years. Parts are still visible to this day and the main station building has been converted into a pleasant house.

The new station was originally called Haughley Road, reflecting the fact that it was not in Haughley but on the road to Haughley. However, it was called Haughley Junction by all the locals and eventually the railway company gave up and changed its name to Haughley Junction in 1890. The point was that Haughley no longer had easy access to the station, which was now a good mile's walk from the village; hence the downturn in village fortunes. It was almost as quick to walk to Stowmarket!

In railway terms the Junction was very important. It was a station where passengers changed trains and where freight was marshalled, but in particular it was

The Flying Scotsman *on a visit to Norfolk, passes under the A11 at Roudham Bridge.*

the exchange point for the night mails. Mail from London, Norwich, Peterborough and the Continent via Harwich, was exchanged for onward movement. The trains were directed on to a loop to keep the main line clear whilst the mailbags were transferred, or the mail vans were unhitched from one train and hitched to another.

Its role as a junction increased with the opening of the Mid-Suffolk Light Railway – the 'Middy'. Milk, produce and schoolchildren used the 'Middy' to Haughley and then changed trains for onward movement to Stowmarket, Ipswich. To cope with the through traffic of trains, freight and passengers Haughley Station has substantial and extensive buildings that remained in use until 1967. There were six platforms, a footbridge, several sidings, two signal-boxes, grain sidings, a goods shed, a goods yard, a turntable and the level crossing. An enormous multi-storey grain drier was built alongside in 1950. Today, the grain drier remains as does a small remnant of the original booking-hall, but as one crosses the level crossing there is nothing else to see.

Thus Haughley never benefited from the railway in the way that other towns and villages with direct access to the railway prospered. Trains no longer stop at Haughley and the infrastructure has disappeared. There is, however, a good collection of local anecdotes from the days of steam trains and not just relating to the time when the 'Middy' overran and crashed through the level-crossing gates.

Mr W.F. Windham, or 'Mad Windham' as he was known, was of aristocratic blood and lived at Felbrigg Hall in Norfolk. He was an exuberant young man who enjoyed a joke and to this end he developed the habit of dressing up in the uniform of the railway company and then impersonating the officials. In mid-1861 he effectively highjacked the train at Haughley where he took over as guard. The train moved down to Stowmarket where Windham signalled for the train to move off before the passengers had finished boarding. Several were thrown back on to the platform and there were many injuries.

In 1874 Mr George Rands established what was probably a first. He was arrested at Haughley after being involved in a noisy and unpleasant argument on the train. Rands had insisted on smoking in a non-smoking compartment and his fellow passengers had complained. Rands had refused to stop smoking and a scuffle ensued.

The late Mr Chaplin, former stationmaster at Haughley Junction, used to describe how working the night mails obviously had its effect. One of the local porters, who had worked for several nights during the week, apparently dozed off in church. A kindly neighbour nudged him to wake him up before the vicar noticed and the porter promptly leapt to his feet in the middle of the church service and announced 'Haughley, Haughley – change here for Finningham, Mellis and all stations to Norwich.'

Commuters were tempted by the advertisements that they saw every day on their way to and from work.

Then, as now, the staff of the railway were important to the image of the company. Good, efficient staff who were polite and helpful could help overcome some of the potential dissatisfaction from the shortfalls in operating standards. Breaches of discipline were treated severely and often meant the loss of employment for the worker.

In days when railways carried a vast range of goods, from poultry and cattle to individual hampers for the landowners of the counties, the temptations for lowly paid staff to divert some of the cargo were considerable. A bottle here and there, shoes, clothing, or the odd chicken or turkey would often not be missed, but if the employee was caught then there was no mercy shown. It was only by establishing reliability and trust that customers could rely on the railways to move their unescorted goods around the country and the total honesty of the railway workforce was an integral part of this business.

Before leaving the railways it is perhaps worth looking back at the leisure and holiday traffic and taking, in particular, a look at Cromer. In the mid-nineteenth century the north of Norfolk was known affectionately as 'Poppyland' but until the coming of the railways it was all but inaccessible to the British public. Cromer was a small village, set in a quiet and beautiful, out-of the-way spot on a remote part of the east coast. The East Norfolk Railway Company constructed the first rail link to Cromer in 1876, but the explosion in Cromer's popularity did not really occur until the Great Eastern Railway Company took over the line in 1881. Their marketing and growing reputation turned the fortunes of the north Norfolk coast and created the start of the tourist industry.

Looking back, the initial investment in the railway was something of a gamble, because, unless the railway was to attract a significant number of new visitors to the

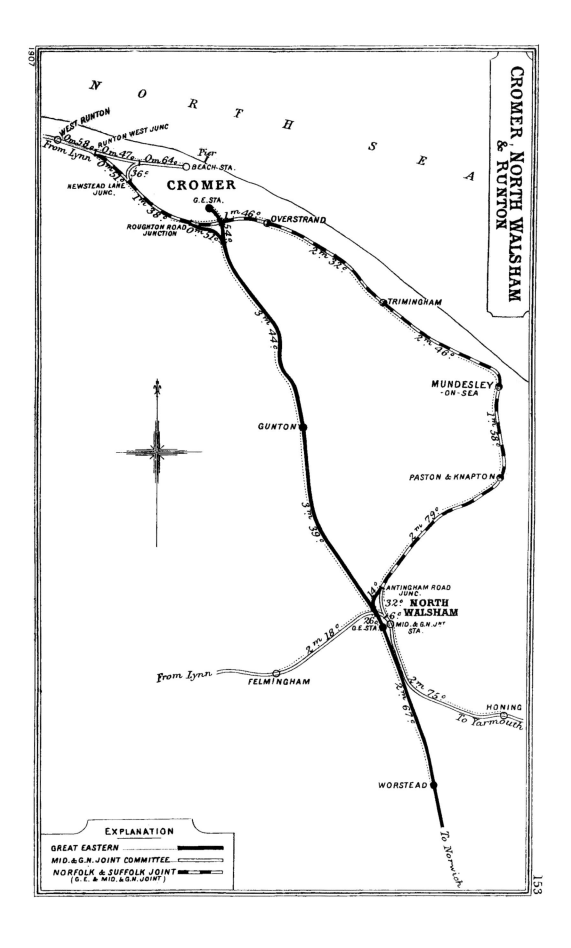

CROMER, NORTH WALSHAM & RUNTON

NORTH SEA

WEST RUNTON
RUNTON WEST JUNC
0m 58c 0m 47c 0m 64c
Pier
From Lynn 0m 3½c
BEACH STA.
36c
NEWSTEAD LANE JUNC.
CROMER
G.E. STA.
1m 38c
ROUGHTON ROAD JUNCTION 0m 51c
1m 54c
1m 46c OVERSTRAND
2m 37c
3m 44c
TRIMINGHAM
2m 46c
MUNDESLEY -ON-SEA
GUNTON
1m 58c
3m 39c
PASTON & KNAPTON
2m 79c
ANTINGHAM ROAD JUNC.
14c
32c NORTH
16c WALSHAM
26c MID. & G.N. JNT STA.
G.E. STA.
2m 18c
From Lynn FELMINGHAM
2m 75c
2m 67c
HONING
To Yarmouth
WORSTEAD
To Norwich

EXPLANATION
GREAT EASTERN ....
MID. & G.N. JOINT COMMITTEE ....
NORFOLK & SUFFOLK JOINT
(G.E. & MID. & G.N. JOINT)

1907

153

area, then it could never be a viable financial proposition. Those early planners must have looked at the natural beauty of the area, the reputedly therapeutic benefits of the North Sea air and its relative proximity to London and to the Midlands, and realised that there was genuine potential to develop holiday trade.

Early seaside holidays from London had centred on the Sussex and Kent coasts with Brighton and Margate being the leading resorts. But people started to grow tired of these over-popular and increasingly expensive venues and looked to the new flexibility that the railways provided to find different holiday destinations.

Having the opportunity thrust upon them, it was then up to the people of Cromer to rise to the challenge. They had to turn their sleepy village into a destination that was worthy of the journey. There had to be hotels, shopping and catering, bathing, and, above all a warm and friendly welcome. All this had to be achieved without detracting too much from the natural beauty and charm of the place, or else the attraction would self-destruct.

The Grand Hotel, an enormous building facing directly onto the sea was completed in 1891. It stood well up on the cliffs and visitors would certainly have found the air invigorating at most times of the year. The 150 guests that it could accommodate had the choice of sea views or views over some of the lovely north Norfolk rolling countryside.

70013 Oliver Cromwell *hauling the* Broadsman *under London Road bridge at Ipswich.*

Thundersley at work. Note the pair of transverse jacks mounted above the front wheels. These locomotives had a habit of de-railing in the sidings and so jacks were provided to enable driver and fireman to jack up the locomotive, wind it across in line with the track and lower it back on the rails.

Close on the heels of the Grand Hotel came the Metropole. This was built in 1894 near the famous parish church of Cromer, in the middle of the town. A Norwich firm (Messrs Trevor, Page & Co.) were responsible for the fitting-out of both hotels and commentary at the time suggests the standards of comfort and quality were extremely high.

From London, the quickest route to Cromer was from Liverpool Street via Ipswich, a journey of 138 miles. Alternatively, it was possible to travel from either Liverpool Street or St Pancras, via Cambridge, this route being about ten miles longer, but bringing the passenger to the much more conveniently situated Cromer Beach Station. There were various excursion ticket options, from a cheap weekend ticket or a two-week return, to a tourist ticket. This last type allowed the passenger to break his journey along the way and was a popular way of seeing a little more of the country. A railway touring holiday in Norfolk might take in Sandringham, Hunstanton, Wells, West Runton, Cromer and Yarmouth! Possibly the traveller might also stop on the return journey at Ely or Cambridge or, on the Ipswich route at Ipswich itself, where the Butter Market was famous, or at Norwich with its fine cathedral.

Norwich boasted three stations: Thorpe, Victoria and Trowse. Thorpe was by far the most imposing and the most important of the stations and the nearby Royal Hotel was already offering accommodation for golfers and for those who wished to explore the Broads.

The fastest trains to Cromer did not actually stop at Norwich but by-passed the city on what was called the 'Wensum Curve'. The 1.30pm express from Liverpool Street arrived at Cromer at 4.25pm. It was a journey time that many would be more than satisfied with today, and this was one hundred and twenty-five years ago. The train was scheduled to be ten vehicles, including a luggage van and a brake van, but the route became so popular that it was often necessary to use up to 17 passenger coaches. Under these conditions the best speeds were not possible and the Great Eastern Railway politely told its passengers that the service might be a few minutes late arriving. However, punctuality was the name of the game and one passenger of 1877, who travelled the line regularly, reported that in an amalgam six return journeys between 1 July and 30 September, the train was a total of two minutes late!

There were two points at which speed had to be restricted: the first was at Ipswich where the train passed over a water-trough and the second, when it had to come to almost a halt to pick up a pilot to cross the Trowse swing-bridge. The only actual stop on the journey was at North Walsham, reached in two hours and forty minutes from London. This was to allow passengers to journey to Mundesley.

The Cromer season was the traditional holiday season of the working and middle classes, July, August and into September, but from quite early on Cromer became a popular destination for breaks out of season. The walks, the churches, and the wild flowers were all attractions and perhaps a spring holiday in April 1877 for the Princess of Wales, the Duke and Duchess of York, Princess Charles of Denmark and Princess Victoria of Wales, helped set the seal of approval on what was to become one of England's prime holiday destinations.

Chapter Six

Steam Afloat

The coastline of some 200 miles and the proximity to the Continent ensured that many of the coastal towns of Norfolk and Suffolk became important ports in earlier times. However, the shape of the coastline and the extent of navigable waterways has changed vastly over the years. Towns such as Wisbech were once busy inland ports but as the rivers silted up the unloading of vessels had to be undertaken closer to the sea.

So it was that Lynn grew to prominence as a port in the fourteenth century. Initially the main goods passing through the port were grain and timber, and much later agricultural machinery. But it also became an important centre for fishing.

Other ports on the north Norfolk coast such as Cley and Wiveton, which today are used mainly for leisure, were once vital links between England and the Continent. Wells-next-the-Sea grew as a fishing and agricultural commerce port. Great Yarmouth was a major port in its own right, both as a mercantile and as a fishing port, specially famed for its herring fleet. But it was also the gateway to the Waveney, Bure and Yare Rivers, which flowed out to sea through its harbour. Thus Norwich, Acle and Beccles became significant ports with the advantage of being nearer to the centres of agricultural or industrial production. In Beccles, Ellist and Garrood built powerful engines (3850hp) based on a special triple-expansion design developed for trawlers. The River Waveney gave easy access from Beccles to the key fishing ports of both Lowestoft and Great Yarmouth.

An early design for a steamship but the problems are already clear – there is not much space left for cargo.

The development of steam-driven ships and boats was a natural progression from the stationary engine and it was the first application of the new source of power outside industry. To trace its history, however, one has to stray some way outside East Anglia.

In effect the engine of a ship is a stationary engine that has been mounted inside a hull. Instead of driving a pump or machine shaft, it drives a shaft with paddles or a propeller attached. Nevertheless it was not until the 1870s that steam really started to replace sail as the principal form of propulsion in ships and boats. The first successful use had been one hundred years earlier by a Frenchman, Marquis de Jouffray. He based his design on Watt's double-acting engine and installed it in a boat, driving paddles through a system of ratchets. The boat was demonstrated on the river at Besancon and successfully made headway against the current. In spite of its success no one really saw the potential of this innovation and, through lack of funds and the effects of the French Revolution, de Jouffray's development ground to a halt.

In England, the patent on Watt's invention held up development. However, before the days of rapid transport and communication, Scotland was relatively remote and it was worth risking an infringement of the laws of patent. Patrick Miller had observed the inefficiency of a man-powered paddleboat, with the crew turning a capstan. He therefore joined up with an imaginative engineer, William Symington, and produced a steam engine based on Watt's design. This they installed in a boat and on a lake at Dalswinton they achieved five miles an hour. The drive to the paddles was a cumbersome arrangement of pulleys and chains but it worked.

They tried to produce a better system, testing an improved version on the Forth-Clyde Canal in 1789, but they could not make it work effectively enough. In desperation they appealed to Watt to help them – a mistake! Watt realised that his patent had been abused and threatened legal action. Miller took fright and withdrew from the business and Symington had no other support or backing and so also had to back out.

As soon as Watt's patent had elapsed in 1800 Symington returned to the steam business. He had a new design and was tasked by the Forth-Clyde Canal Company to build a tug. This new boat, 56 feet long and 18 feet in the beam, was named the *Charlotte Dundas* and was launched in 1801, undergoing trials in the Forth-Clyde Canal in 1802. There were several innovations in the design, which used a single cylinder, double-acting engine that developed ten horsepower. The great weight of the engine was counter-balanced by the weight of the boiler, which was mounted on the opposite side of the hull. The drive was provided by a rear-mounted paddle wheel driven though a crankshaft direct from the engine. This became the model for all paddle-steamers, no matter if the paddles were on the side of the hull or mounted at the rear of the boat.

The demonstrations were amazingly successful and it looked as if the break-through had been made. The Duke of Bridgewater, who was pushing hard for much more canal development, ordered eight of the new tugs, but he died before the order could be taken up. It was then discovered that the wash from the *Charlotte Dundas* was creating considerable damage to the banks of the canal and so operations ceased. The tug was laid up and abandoned and finally broken up in 1861. Many could see

A typical paddle-steamer used all around the British coast.

the potential but no one could put the theory into practice, there were just too many problems and not enough backers to fund the research and development needed.

It was not until Trevithick developed engines that could withstand much higher pressures that real progress was made. He built an engine, which used a water feed pump rather than a condenser and which worked at a pressure of 40lbs per square inch, a miracle in its time, and installed it in a dredger for use in the East India Docks. It was a success and worked for many years, but Trevithick was tempted away from boats to the developments on the road and especially on the railways.

The challenge was taken up by Matthew Murray and he began a steamboat service between Norwich and Great Yarmouth. The service ran for four years from 1813 but came to an abrupt and tragic end when a boiler explosion claimed several lives and effectively closed down the service.

Although most of the early attempts to apply steam power to boats was on the inland waterways, the dream of steam-driven, sea-going ships was always present. Woolf, of the London-based company Edwards & Woolf, designed and patented a new engine in 1810. This was a compound marine engine and was much more efficient in its use of steam, passing steam from the first cylinder into a second and using it again. The idea had been around for a long time, but like so many of the steam developments it was hampered because of Watt's patent. Although Watt usually gets the credit for the early development of the steam engine, it is interesting to speculate how differently the world of steam might have developed had Watt not registered his patent. He guarded the development jealously and zealously and inhibited some very good ideas in the process.

Woolf's engine was an important step towards sea-borne steam power and another London firm, Maudslay, started to design engines for boats and ships but there were still many hurdles to be overcome. The most obvious was that ships were still timber-built and there was an inherent risk of fire. The second was that steam engines had still not reached any great efficiency and it took a lot of coal to power an engine. For a voyage of any length it would need a hold full of coal, leaving no room for cargo. Finally, fresh water needed to be carried in vast quantities because the seawater caused rapid corrosion when it was used to condense the steam.

The work started by Miller and Symington in Scotland was never totally abandoned. By 1811, Henry Bell, who had joined up with Symington, designed an engine which was paired with a boiler by David Napier, and these were mounted into a small steamboat named *The Comet*. She was used to provide a service on the Clyde from Glasgow to Helensburgh, and visitors to the Science Museum in London can now admire *The Comet*, displayed as the first successful British steamboat.

The success of *The Comet* was the turning point, and things started to move quickly. She was followed by the *Margery*, the first cross-channel steamer, and in 1821 the larger, 90-ton *Rob Roy* started service on the Dover–Calais route. In the same year Aaron Manby constructed a ship of riveted iron plate and so overcame the greatest risk, that of fire. The ship took the name of the builder and was pressed into service carrying cargo from London to Paris.

As engines became more powerful, so ships increased in size and the Clyde started to develop its reputation for the construction of modern shipping. Napier built the *Superb* at 240 tons, and the *Eclipse* powered by two 35hp engines. Meanwhile a name that was to become a legend in shipbuilding also made its first appearance – that of Brunel. In fact it was Marc Brunel, father of Isambard Kingdom, who invented a condenser that could remove the salt from seawater. The age of ocean-going steamers was dawning. The iron keel for the younger Brunel's *Great Britain* was laid in 1839, although it took thirteen years to build, remaining in service between England and Australia until 1886.

Some statistics from those early days of steamships give a good idea of the scale of the problems that the designers and builders faced. The *Bernice* steamed from Falmouth to Bombay in 1837. She took eighty-eight days to complete the voyage of which no less than twenty-five were spent in coaling stations along the way. Brunel's *Great Eastern* was built to carry the 10 000 tons of coal needed to complete the two-way journey to Australia. In fact, she never achieved the efficiency required of a commercial vessel and was used to lay the first trans-Atlantic cables.

After about 1860 iron hulls became the norm. Engines working at much higher pressures provided greater efficiency and power and the true age of

Brunel's Great Britain *as she now lies at Bristol.*

steamships arrived. Britain led the world and the development of the steam-driven merchant fleet, protected by a steam-powered Royal Navy, brought much prosperity to Britain.

However, as ships became larger and faster, so the advances in technology enabled the construction of relatively small and light engines for other uses. Ellist and Garrood of Beccles built a range of powerful, compact engines. They were based on a special triple-expansion design and were used to power the trawlers of the fleets at Great Yarmouth and Lowestoft.

In a rare departure from agricultural and road machinery, Ransomes built an iron propeller steamer, launched at their Orwell works in 1851. The region's rivers remained important arteries, with barges carrying goods from all over Norfolk and Suffolk to the seaports. There were few locks because of the predominantly low-lying nature of the countryside and navigation was straightforward. The surprise is that, in two counties with ideal river communications, steam river transport was slow to develop.

The River Lark was navigable, through ten locks, for some 19 miles via Icklingham and Barton Mills to Mildenhall and, at one time, via a canal to Bury St Edmunds. The waterway was restored in 1898 but rapidly fell into decay and reverted to a short branch from Tuddenham Mill to the River Lark at Barton Mills.

Barges on the Little Ouse or Brandon River came to within three miles of Thetford – they used to go right into town but the town corporation failed to

A steam cargo barge (now restored). Such vessels were generally too large for the tiny waterways of Norfolk and Suffolk, where the Norfolk wherries and Suffolk lighters prevailed.

An 1890s Grasshopper Engine, built by Day & Summers of Southampton to drive a floating bridge. Such engines were mounted on one side of the hull and the boiler on the other to achieve stability.

provide the necessary funding to maintain the navigation. The waterway was 22 miles long and the passage was through eight locks. As suggested earlier in this work, Brandon was, in those days, of considerable importance to the defence industry because it was almost the only source of gunflints in the country. If you consider that all the guns of the early nineteenth century were flintlock weapons and that a flint lasted anything from eight to fifteen shots, then you can understand why transport from this Norfolk town was very important. There was also a separate cut, up Brandon Creek to the Fison's Vitriol and Manure Works. Again, the waterway was worked by wide-beamed, shallow-drafted fen lighters and not by steam vessels.

It was possible to follow the Stowmarket and Ipswich Navigation from the Orwell to Stowmarket and as far as Dagworth, by Haughley. The River Bure linked Aylsham, Coltishall, Wroxham and, via a number of dykes and canals, many other towns and villages to Yarmouth.

The River Stour was navigable to Sudbury. This was a significant waterway of some 35 miles with 15 locks. Here the locks were built to a larger size than elsewhere, with a 95-foot length allowing two 47-foot lighters in the lock at the same time.

The River Waveney took barges to Beccles and Bungay under several railway swing-bridges. There were few stretches with a tow-path and the traffic was almost entirely Norfolk sailing wherries.

The River Yare was the largest natural waterway in the area with good depth and reasonable width. There was no need for locks and Norfolk sailing wherries and steamships used the route for access to Norwich and especially to the New Mills there. There was a much narrower and shallower link to the mills at Loddon, via the River Chet, which joined the River Yare at Hardley Cross. In addition, many smaller navigations made it possible to work smaller boats to the heads of navigations and up narrow access cuts or canals to mills, farms and minor factories.

The Great Eastern Railway had an early interest in the waterways and took over the Norwich Navigation Company as early as 1827. They opened up or adapted parts of the waterway between Norwich and Lowestoft, including the building of the two-mile New Cut between the River Yare at Reedham and the River Waveney at Haddiscoe.

There were several reasons why steam never seriously competed for the river-traffic role. The locks, which were mostly on the upper reaches of the navigations, were small and could usually accept just one barge at a time. The barges themselves were shallow drafted to cope with the shallow waterways, and to put a steam engine in them would have been to halve the cargo space. It was only a practical option if the steam barge could haul a further 'dead' barge or 'butty' behind. Due to the small locks this meant 'double locking' – taking one barge through at a time – and this was wasteful in time, energy and water, which in the process was drained from the upper reaches. In such circumstances the horse-drawn barges and sailing barges were as fast if not faster than the steam barge and certainly more economical.

Grebe (later Otto*) was built by Forrest & Sons of Wivenhoe in Essex and for many years graced the Norfolk waterways. She is now maintained at the Windermere Steamboat Museum, an elegant example of Victorian/Edwardian leisure.*

Norfolk keels, Norfolk wherries and Suffolk lighters, all of similar broad-beam, shallow-draft construction, prevailed on the waterways of Norfolk and Suffolk whilst the steam revolution took place around them. It was only with the coming of the diesel and petrol marine engines that these fine old craft disappeared.

Coasters such as this were a frequent sight up and down the Norfolk and Suffolk coast.

However, if the barges themselves did not need steam power, the infrastructure that supported the inland waterways relied heavily on steam. Much of the dredging was carried out by steam-driven dredgers or by ploughing engines using a mud scoop. Dockside cranes were increasingly steam driven and the onward modes of transport by ship, rail or road were all reliant on steam power.

At sea sailing ships and luggers made up the fishing fleets until well into the second half of the nineteenth century. The early use of steam by the industry came when steam tugs were used to haul sailing vessels out of port against the wind; once in clear water they could fend for themselves. The early steam tugs were all paddle-driven boats with considerable power. They were seaworthy in their own right and were occasionally used in periods of calm or adverse wind conditions to cross to the Continent and haul back stranded sailing vessels.

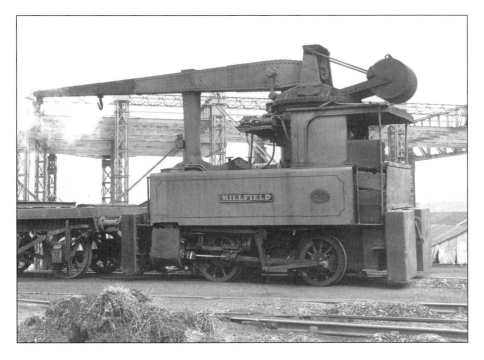

Millfield – a purpose-built dockside crane. This is a relatively modern piece of steam engineering, built in 1942 by Robert Stephenson and Hawthorn and weighing some 36 tons.

Lydia Era *leaves Great Yarmouth. This splendidly restored relic from the vast fleets of Great Yarmouth and Lowestoft was restored by the Maritime Trust.*

Courtesy of The Eastern Daily Press

Steam trawlers were introduced in 1881 and the sailing trawler rapidly disappeared from the scene. First attempts were to construct paddle-steamers for trawling but it was soon found that these were not up to the rougher seas, especially the North Sea conditions encountered by the Norfolk and Suffolk crews, and so it was not long before the design changed to the screw propeller. Once these came into service the steam trawlers were far less weather-dependent and could travel greater distances with comparative ease. They did need larger crews, but in terms of productivity there was no comparison.

Whilst the proximity of the fishing ports of north-east England to the coalfields of the region made it much easier and more economical for ports such as North Shields to prosper, it was soon evident that the only way to compete in the developing industry was to turn to steam.

Coal was brought to the ports both by coaster and by rail. In the case of rail, the return leg meant that there was a ready means of transport to move the fish back to the industrial heartland of England. The advent of steam trawlers heralded the massive exploitation of the North Sea. Sailing drifters lingered on into the twentieth century but by the First World War all the fleets had effectively been converted to steam. Catches improved dramatically and figures for Britain as a whole show that from a total annual catch in the order of 12 000 tons in 1860, the catch rose to nearer 500 000 tons in 1912.

The normal method of fishing was by beam trawl and this lasted until 1894 when the otter-trawl board was introduced. The problem with the beam trawl was that in order to increase the size of the net, it was necessary to increase the size and strength of the beam, and the winch gear could not cope effectively with the extra weight. The otter-trawl board dispensed with the beam and by means of a pair of angled 'doors' opened out the net as the water pressure reacted on the 'doors'.

It was the combination of the more efficient trawler and drifter trades and the coming of the railways that brought great change to the fishing industries of Norfolk and Suffolk. Before the railways fish had to be consumed close to the port. Now it could be taken considerable distances and be in the market or on the fishmonger's slab within a few hours. Ice was either stored from winter in ice-houses or it was imported from Norway, and this made the transportation even easier and more flexible.

Deep-sea trawlers and the power available to manage the nets led to the discovery of the North Sea 'Great Silver Pits'. The use of steam winches, enabling much heavier fishing gear to be used, also contributed to fishing becoming more effective and efficient.

Fish for the consumer became plentiful and from being a luxury item it quickly became a part of the staple diet of the poor. Herring in particular gave good nutritional value at a very low price. Millions of barrels were taken by rail to London and the fish were so frequently eaten by the poorer people that the smell of herring became synonymous with squalor and poverty.

It was the ready availability of fish in the towns that gave rise to the fried fish trade. Potatoes had been fried in the Lancashire mills as a quick and filling meal for the women working in the mills. The custom spread and, once fresh fish was readily available, the two items became a staple of the British diet. It can thus be said that the railways had effectively introduced fish and chips.

In Lowestoft, the Consolidated Steam Fishing & Ice Company (later Consolidated Fisheries Ltd) owned an enormous fleet of trawlers. When combined with their trawlers in other British ports, it became the largest fishing fleet in the world. With its virtual monopoly on the landing of white fish and the vast employment opportunities, not only at sea but also in the support of the operation, it was a vital part of the local economy.

The fleet needed provisions, repairs and maintenance as well as the fuel. There was ready work for ships' chandlers, riveters and platers, tinsmiths, blacksmiths, plumbers, pipe fitters, boiler makers, joiners, shipwrights, net-makers and rope and cable makers. As time went on skilled engineers were also required for wireless fitting and operation and for all sorts of instrumentation.

Life for the trawlerman was hard and basic. The discomforts and dangers are almost unimaginable, especially when the trawlers were operating well away from their home ports above the Arctic Circle. Sleeping accommodation comprised bunks crammed into the forward part of the hull. Eating would be around a tapered table squeezed between the rows of bunks and the whole area was heated by a small, solid-fuel stove. In bad weather men were strapped into their bunks to prevent them being thrown around as the bow rose and fell in the violent seas.

On duty and on deck it was often very cold and exceedingly dangerous. The trawlers braved the worst of the weather, sometimes having to admit to being second temporarily and heading into the wind and the seas to survive afloat. Waves would sweep over the deck and it was not unusual for the trawlerman to be standing thigh deep in ice-cold water.

Just as in steam ploughing where there was an enormous danger from the breaking of a ploughing cable, so there was a danger from the cables that dragged the trawl nets. If one should snap, and they regularly did, the cable would whiplash back and was quite capable of cutting a man in two. Bringing in the net, especially in heavy seas, was the most dangerous time; the boat would have to be held steady and could then drift side-on to the sea. It would rock from side to side so the working gunwale might be under water one minute and 12 feet in the air the next. The loss of fingers and hands, or even complete limbs, was not unusual. Skin was weathered and leathery. Boils and chaffing from the oilskins were a routine problem.

The Royal Navy had vast numbers of steam trucks, engines and cranes to support the fleet. It was the flooding of the market with second-hand machinery that brought the price of trucks and traction engines down to an affordable cost for the average farmer or haulier.

practical machine in Britain, in 1867. This was a massive 30-ton roller, which the company supplied for the Corporation of Liverpool, but the roller was too heavy and instead of rolling the road and bedding in the ballast, it crushed the ballast into fine particles and so the road lost a good deal of its stability.

There followed a number of other experiments, including the introduction of the three-wheeled roller, which gave much better stability to the machine – the early two-wheeled or tandem machines could quite easily roll on to their side. In the end, it was a simple design that proved best, with the boiler arrangement very much along the lines of the early portable engines and a simple chain-drive mechanism to the driving wheels. Steering followed the traction-engine principles with a worm-gear-and-chain arrangement. Once Aveling had produced a usable machine, others soon followed.

The advantages of the steamroller were quickly evident in the quality of the roads that were being produced, and the demand for them grew steadily in the 1880s and 1890s. Here was a strange paradox: at the time, in the early twentieth century, when the internal combustion engine was starting to oust steam from the haulage and road transport industries, it was the requirement for better roads that boosted the demand for steam and steamrollers.

A Robey tandem roller – now at Bressingham. Such rollers were inherently unstable and it was only when road surfaces became more modern and firm that these tandem rollers could be used safely.

The steering mechanism that was to become the standard for almost all traction engines and steamrollers.

Buster, Bressingham's 1924 Burrell road roller. Officially classified as a ten-ton roller, it in fact weighs 12 tons. It was built in Thetford by Burrell and owned and operated by Doran Bros also of Thetford. There are only two known surviving examples of this class of roller.

At first the rollers were simply used to make a better job of compacting the traditional roads, but cars and trucks were now starting to move rather more quickly and dust became a major problem. It was necessary to look to other materials to improve the surfaces and to give an all-weather capability. Tarred roads started to become the norm. In the villages of Norfolk and Suffolk, it still took a long time for such 'modern' methods to be employed. There are still older folk around today who can remember vividly the village street being tarred for the first time in the 1920s.

Steamrollers thus became a common sight all over the two counties. Like other steam plant, such as the threshing equipment and ploughing engines, steamrollers were usually owned by a single contractor in the locality and hired out as needed. The change from granite to chippings and shingle, and the introduction of tarmac itself, called for lighter rollers, especially for finishing the surfaces, and the tow roller or tandem roller came back into use for this purpose. Now used on a flat surface, and not in danger of tipping over, these machines overcame their early unpopularity.

The steamroller outlived all its companions and was the last type of steam engine in frequent use on the roads, eventually being replaced by diesel rollers at about the same time as the last steam locomotives were being taken out of service on the railways.

The first serious attempt at providing steam-driven haulage was also made in France, in 1771, when Nicholas Gugnot produced a steam tractor to haul cannons. The first

Part of the road gang with their ten-ton Fowler roller.

Early haulage by traction engine.

attempt was a failure, the engine being unable to generate sufficient power to haul the heavy guns, but a subsequent heavier and more powerful version was recognised as the first step towards effective haulage.

Although the French had a head start, the idea was not followed up in France. The French Revolution impeded further development and so the idea was next taken up in England by Richard Trevithick. Trevithick had been much involved in the development of the steam engine and he ranks alongside Robert Stephenson for importance in the development of a self-mobile steam vehicle. Nevertheless, development was slow. James Watt's patent ran until 1800. But Watt was only interested in stationary engines and could not appreciate the need for higher boiler pressures that were to be needed for self-propelled vehicles.

In 1803 Trevithick constructed a steam carriage which was put on trial in London. The design was based very much on the existing form of transport – the horse-drawn carriage or coach. This early steam carriage was a strange-looking machine with enormous driving wheels some ten feet in diameter and a single front wheel for steerage, rather like an old-fashioned invalid car. It had room for eight passengers who had to clamber high up on to the top of the vehicle. The fireman stood on a platform at the rear of the vehicle and kept the fire stoked. The carriage was said to achieve 12mph.

Although the carriage worked, it was not seen to have any advantage over the horse and so Trevithick was unable to find anyone to put up the money for

Trevithick's design for a steam engine.

further development. He turned his attention to the idea of railways – some time ahead of Stephenson!

The Napoleonic Wars, the state of the roads and some fairly entrenched thinking all combined to obstruct progress. Potential inventors failed to tackle the main problem, which was to devise a system of gears that would convert the power from the engine into a revolutionary motion to drive the wheels. The other problem was to get the boiler weight down to a practical level whilst achieving higher boiler pressures. As a result, boilers were made with thinner shells and a system of tubes was developed to expose a greater surface area of water to the heat. This was to become the principle for the development of all self-propelled steam engines.

Apart from the state of the roads, the biggest problem was the tremendous resistance to change from those who operated horse-drawn transport. There were some early attempts to set up regular passenger services, notably by Goldsworthy Gurney, and then by Walter Hancock, but neither system stayed long in service. The horse had prevailed for so long as the only effective means of land transport that there was an understandable affection for the horse and a real fear and suspicion over these rather noisy and messy new steam machines. They seemed dangerous and anti-social and, what's more, caused many accidents by scaring horses.

There was an extensive network of stagecoach services across the country, employing a large number of drivers, ostlers and innkeepers. The spread and growing success of the railways was also an obstacle to developments in road transport. The railway operators, already making great inroads into the business of the stagecoach companies, were now to combine with those companies to oppose the development of road transport. The cause of road haulage was not helped by a series of accidents and, after a particularly bad accident on a service introduced

Routine maintenance. Note the rubber tyres for road work.

An 1896 Thorneycroft bus/van.

National Motor Museum, Beaulieu

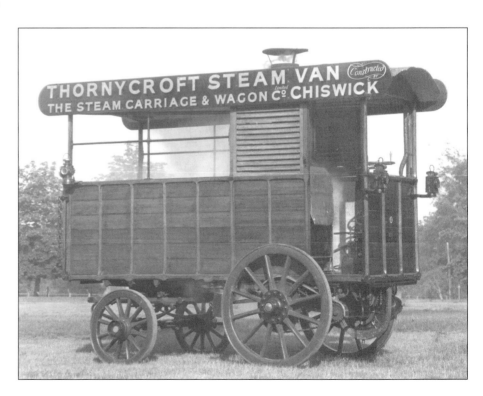

In the 1950s steam was still seen occasionally on the road.

between Glasgow and Paisley, the Court of Sessions passed a bye-law forbidding the use of steam vehicles on the public highways.

Nevertheless, the growing wealth of the nation, the development of industry and a burgeoning population brought transport requirements far beyond those that could be met by the stagecoaches and the early railways. A major breakthrough came with the invention of the Macadam road surface. At last there was a hardwearing and smooth surface that allowed vehicles to travel at higher speeds in relative safety. But it was still a difficult business to move steamers on the roads. Several other legal restrictions were put in place and high tolls were charged for the heavier loads in particular.

By about 1880, the thinking had progressed to the stage where it was realised that three different solutions were required to provide steam power on the roads: there needed to be a system that was capable of providing public transport and light haulage, a system capable of heavy haulage, and there was a need for a very light form of transport – the motor car.

The motor car was to have a short life as part of the Steam Age. It took a long time to develop the boilers and engines that met the requirements of compact size and lightness. Such engines also had to generate adequate speed and reliability to give advantage over the horse. No sooner had this been achieved than the internal combustion engine was invented and developed and the steam engine was out of a job!

A 1901 locomotive steam car.

An 1897 Soame steam car, seen here restored and presented in a rally in 1956. The simple body and the wheels clearly owe their design to the farm cart.

The car was really developed first in France. Here there was much less legislation against steam vehicles and so there was more freedom to experiment. There were three key names at the time: Bollée, De Dion and Serpollet. They each produced a number of experimental vehicles. Bollée failed to overcome the weight problem and so failed to match the speed and compactness of his rivals, but he did make significant advances in vehicle construction. It was De Dion who teamed up with Bouton and produced the first really practical steam car in 1883. The partnership did well and they went on to produce a large number of steam cars and steam cycles.

In England the idea was taken up by Rudge who produced a steam tricycle that used a Bouton engine and could achieve 25mph. However, some now-famous names were starting to appear in the development of the internal combustion engine: Benz, Panhard-Levasseur, and the only serious on-going production of steam cars was by the Stanley brothers in the United States. After some early problems and some changes of ownership, the Stanley Company became the most successful of all steam-car producers. Many were exported and could still be seen on the roads of Norfolk and Suffolk as late as the mid-1920s. The Stanley cost just £150, was very quick to raise steam using a new type of oil-burning boiler, was quiet and could cruise at 30mph.

An apparently unusual military variant, but the idea is still used to this day. In the Yugoslav wars of the 1990s many modern diesel tractors were converted to scout and armoured cars in exactly the same way. The advantage the traction engine had was that it could take a considerable weight of armour and so the crew were much better protected than their modern counterparts.

By 1911 more names were appearing in the motor world, not least Rolls Royce in England and Ford in America. But there was still one remarkable steam-car designer who carried on – Abner Doble. His cars were individually produced, they had an enormous operating range and could reach 100mph. They used the same type of oil-burning flash boilers and, with up to four cylinders, raising steam was the business of just a few minutes. Doble finally gave up the struggle against the internal combustion engine in 1932, when he transferred to Sentinels.

Generally, steam cars were just reaching their peak of safety, design and operating efficiency when they were displaced by the petrol engine.

The manufacturers of steam engines managed an incredible juggling act, producing many different types of engines and in considerable numbers. Avelings are recorded as having produced over 5500 engines between 1909 and 1924 and of

A Sentinel steam truck. Originally designed to travel at the 16mph speed limit, later versions of these remarkable vehicles could travel at well over 30mph.

these some 290 were steam wagons – the forerunner of the modern truck. In about the same period, Burrells of Thetford produced 114 steam wagons.

From 1910 onwards manufacturers started to see that the real future of steam on the roads was in the production of steam wagons, and some companies started to specialise in their production. Firms such as Atkinson and Thorneycroft started making their names in the haulage industry at this time. Demand rose to a peak during the First World War but then fell away sharply in 1919, to the point when only Sentinel and Foden were left in competition with the new manufacturers of petrol-engined trucks. It was also the First World War that effectively saw the end to speed restrictions. The 1905 Road Transport Act had limited speeds to five mph and manufacturers rated their trucks as having a top speed of six mph, although almost all trucks could comfortably exceed this.

The increased demand for road supply during the war effectively raised the speed limit to 16mph and the increased control provided by the Ackermann steering principle, and the improvements in design, made these speeds quite safe and realistic.

During the 1920s, design improved at a dramatic rate and Foden trucks, with their lower price compared with Sentinel, were the more numerous. The classic truck of this era was the Speed Six. This was a twin-rear-axle, six-wheel truck that was

A lighter truck.

Winter work for a Sentinel steam tractor.

designed to reach 45mph, but in fact was so successfully designed that it could achieve 60mph! Sentinel also produced a six-wheeler in both ten-ton and five-ton tipper versions. It was designed as a robust truck to travel at the 16mph limit, but was also capable of rather more.

Generally regarded as the finest steam truck ever built, the Sentinel 'S' model was developed in the 1930s. This amazing vehicle continued production in Czechoslovakia during and after the Second World War and the last recorded batch were delivered to Argentina in 1950. The vehicle was produced in four-, six- and

Bressingham's Sentinel timber tractor, restored to full working order in 2002.

Alan Bloom drives his Foden steam truck.

eight-wheel versions both as a flat bed, conventional truck and as a tipper. The engine, originally a duplex-cylinder engine, was replaced by a four-in-line model, which worked on a single crankshaft – an idea stolen from the internal combustion engine. Although the law now allowed speeds of up to 20mph, these trucks could cruise comfortably at 50mph.

Suffolk's contribution to this part of the story came from Garrett. In 1926 they produced the 'Regal Six', a truck that combined a number of excellent features. It was powered by a duplex-cylinder engine and had side- and end-tipping gear powered by a hydraulic system. It was a superb truck by standards of the time but sadly it did not compete well with the better-known Sentinel and the cheaper Foden; production lasted just four years.

Running these monsters was a logistic nightmare in itself. The Garrett, which developed 120-brake horsepower, used 435 gallons of water per mile. The fully laden weight of 23 tons could be accelerated from a standstill to 10mph in six seconds, to 20mph in twenty-three seconds and to 30mph in seventy-one seconds. Importantly, it had very efficient steam-operated brakes that could stop the vehicle at 20mph in just 28 feet.

Both Sentinel and Foden made steam tractors, although it is the Sentinel that is perhaps the more famous. In particular the timber tractors were wonderful vehicles with the ability to winch out trees from the felling area. They were very compact vehicles weighing 11 tons and having large pneumatic tyres to provide a good off-road capability. They had a good range of gears and were very powerful. The tractors could cruise almost in silence at 35mph on the roads. Only 12 of these specialist vehicles were ever built, one of which can be seen in steam at Bressingham Steam Museum today.

Steam wagons had developed in parallel with the bicycle and, as a result, it was a common sight around the roads of Norfolk and Suffolk to see cyclists indulging in a highly dangerous but efficacious practice of hitching a lift. It would be quite normal to see a steam wagon travelling at 15mph with a cyclist hanging on to the tailboard chains. Alan Bloom, the founder of Bressingham, well remembers one such 'lift' that took him over 30 effortless but hazardous miles.

One might expect the natural development from the steam wagon to be the steam bus but, although buses were produced in quite large numbers (there were over 200 operating in London alone), they were never really a success. Again the Suffolk contribution came from Garrett, who produced a bus that was so quiet, no one could hear it coming and as a result it became law for buses to be fitted with klaxon horns.

In Ipswich and Great Yarmouth, the Great Eastern Railway Company introduced steam tramways, trying to bring railway technology to the roads. These were successful for a while as a means of transport but proved uneconomic to run, the investments and the on-going running costs resulting in fares too high to be competitive.

Design improvements, marked environmental advantages, and fast steam-raising (ten minutes from cold) should all have helped the steam engine to compete with

A practical Foden truck built in 1936. It had a working pressure of 1500lbs psi and used a 'Doble' principle engine.

A remarkably modern-looking steamer. These sophisticated six-wheelers were designed to travel at up to 45mph but many a driver has pushed them up to 60mph!

the petrol engine, but in the end it was the logistics that gave the internal combustion engine the edge. In comparison with the steam buses, petrol-engine buses could travel many miles without refuelling or requiring attention and so, in spite of the fumes and the noise, they became the preferred vehicles.

Steam wagons never really developed to the stage where they could cope with heavy haulage and it fell to the traction engine to carry out this work. Garretts of Leiston and Burrells of Thetford were among about a dozen manufacturers who produced traction engines in quantity. Burrells also produced the prototype fairground engine – the Showman. In this type the traditional traction engine was fitted with decorative brass and brightly coloured paintwork. A generator was combined to power fairground equipment and a crane was often added to help handle some of the bulky fairground equipment.

These engines could weigh up to 20 tons and could haul a train of five wagons over a considerable distance. They performed reliably and effectively until the late 1930s but by then the diesel tractors were coming to the fore and the steam engines were forgotten. Many were scrapped, others in excellent operational condition were sold for less than £100. It would have been a good investment, for a similar engine today would cost a collector in excess of £100 000.

If there was enough manoeuvring space, traction engines could haul enormous 'trains'.

Chapter Eight

Accidents & The Law

S team engines were massive pieces of machinery. The power they were capable of producing, the weight of the engines, the enormous internal pressures generated and the early state of the technology, all made it inevitable that accidents would happen – and happen they did!

Some were amusing, many were tragic. Some were 'acts of God', others were very much man-made. Boiler explosions were not unusual and were almost invariably fatal. The operator or driver would be positioned right beside or behind the boiler, which would, without warning, simply explode like some giant grenade. Where this was the fault of a weakness in the metal, or the build up of corrosion, there was little that could be done to prevent the accident, but sometimes it was because the operator wanted to squeeze that little extra power out of his machine and he would wind down the safety valve. It was a practice that he had used perhaps hundreds of times before, but when he overdid it or when this act coincided with a weakening of an aging boiler, the results were often catastrophic.

Accidents on the railway were the most publicised, partially because they were open to the public and members of the public were regularly involved in the accidents, and partly because there was an almost ghoulish interest in seeing just how bad the railway companies could be. Driver error was often at the root of the railway accidents and excessive speed was often a major, if not the only, contributory factor. As early as 1845 a Norwich-bound express left the rails and tumbled down the embankment near Harling Road. Both the driver and the fireman were killed and the subsequent enquiry, although raising some question about the serviceability of the locomotive, found that speed was the main cause.

Sometimes the mistakes were very basic. Three years later a passenger train from Newmarket was halted at Dullingham and the locomotive was detached from the train. Unfortunately, no one had thought to apply the brakes and the laden passenger wagons started to roll back down the three-mile hill to Newmarket. It is a long and relatively steep hill in railway terms and fortunately there was no other train on the line. The runaway simply continued to gather speed until it eventually crashed into the buffers at Newmarket, where it had started. Miraculously, no one was killed and there were only a few serious injuries.

The lessons were not learned and a train on the 'Middy' was allowed to roll down the gradient and into the level crossing at Haughley Junction. Again it was fortunate that no one was hurt and that no other train or road vehicle was involved.

Although technically out of the region as far as this book is concerned, one of the worst railway accidents was at Witham Station in 1905. A track gang was working on the track and failed to restore it to a usable state as the express approached. The

The Cromer Express *crash, 1 September 1905. A combination of bad maintenance work and high speed caused this horrific 'pile up' and amazingly, although the train was well-laden, only 11 passengers were killed.*

Another frightening sight, this time at Lavenham on 15 October 1891. Incredibly, there were only minor injuries to the three crewmen and to three passengers, all of whom had recovered within a week.

Cromer Express left the rails at high speed. The wreckage was awful and how only 11 people from the crowded train were killed can only be a mystery when one sees photographs of the accident.

On 15 October 1891 the 4.05pm, the Bury to Marks Tey train rolled off the track at Lavenham. A stretch of rail that had been re-laid three years before gave way and the locomotive (No. 169, an 0-4-4 tank engine), the brake van, four carriages and a horsebox literally capsized. All three railwaymen – the driver, fireman and guard – were injured but none seriously and all made quick recoveries. There were only 15 passengers on the train and of these only three suffered minor injuries – an extraordinarily lucky escape for all.

There were also many cases of tragic accidents involving children, farm workers and animals. It was too easy to wander on to the track and unfortunately it was the last act of a good number of people.

In 1894 there was a first for Norfolk. Although the swing-bridges were built to carry the railways over the rivers of Norfolk, the Norfolk wherries usually did not have to trouble the bridge keeper. As the wherry approached the bridge, the sail would be lowered and the mast dropped. The wherryman would then 'shoot' the bridge with the aid of his quant pole. This was the plan as the wherry *Topaz* approached the swing-bridge at Somerleyton. The wherryman had probably passed under the bridge hundreds of times before. Anyone who has boated on the Broads will know that there are just inches to spare on some of the lower bridges, and it seems to the uninitiated that the boat must hit the bridge. On this occasion there was no cargo in the hold and the tide, which had been higher than normal, had been held up by the strong winds. *Topaz* struck the bridge a hefty blow. The bridge was strong enough to stand it and a few minutes later a goods train passed safely over the top of the scene, but subsequent trains were stopped until the damage could be inspected and the repairs completed.

A few miles away at Reedham bridge a potential disaster was averted, by chance rather than by any particular action. It was often the case that disaffected employees would take revenge on their employers by committing some act of sabotage. In a rural community this might be the burning of a haystack or the setting loose of livestock. With a railway it was rather more difficult to find a practical means of revenge. At Reedham, and at the other swing-bridges, priority was given to the river traffic. Just a few minutes were allowed in each hour for the bridge to be closed and the railway to operate over the bridge. To secure the bridge in place there was a system of pins and level adjusters, which were operated by large spanners. One employee, who had a grudge against the railway company, deliberately laid the spanners across the line in an attempt to derail the locomotive. Fortunately the attempt failed, probably because the speed limit over the bridge was only four mph and, as soon as the sound from the wheels scraping against the spanners was heard and the bridge started to vibrate, the driver managed to stop.

Heavy snow in the winter of 1854 was the catalyst for a series of misunderstandings that eventually led to a serious accident near Thetford. With time taking the sadness out of the tragedy, the story sounds rather like a Hoffnung tale – 'half way up he met the barrel coming down!' There are various accounts and the detail in these, and the detail from the evidence in the subsequent court case, differ so markedly that it is difficult to discern what really did happen. The snow was unusually heavy, the telegraph system was out of order and it was not known if the line between Thetford and Harling, which was particularly badly affected by the snow, was still passable. The Thetford stationmaster decided that he ought to establish contact and find out if the line was open and so he sent a locomotive to Harling. The correct line in the Harling direction was the 'down' line, and it was decided to use the 'down' line, in both directions because the stationmaster at Thetford could ensure that no further

A goods train accident at Sudbury in about 1900.

traffic moved on to that stretch of line. The guard on the locomotive going to Harling was to tell the stationmaster at Harling to stop any trains on the 'up' line and prevent them from leaving Harling. The locomotive was then to return to Thetford on the 'down' line, i.e. in the wrong direction.

The situation was then complicated by the unexpected arrival of a special train from Cambridge that had been sent to pick up stranded passengers from Thetford and beyond. The train was hauled by two locomotives. How or why is not clear, but the officer who had actually given the orders to the guard on his way to Harling, now set off on the footplate of the special train. The train proceeded on the wrong track, the 'up' track, because it was known that the locomotive that had been sent to Harling would return on the 'down' track. To complicate matters further, a second special train arrived at Harling. The train, which had come from Norwich, also had two locomotives and carried two senior officers of the railway company. It was explained to them that the stationmaster at Thetford had ordered all trains to be stopped at Harling, but they decided to overrule him and set off on the 'up' line towards Thetford. At Bridgham, in the snow at dusk, the two trains on the 'up' line suddenly came in sight of each other. The drivers of the leading locomotives and the officer who had broken his own orders, jumped clear and escaped with light injuries, but the two trains ran head-on into each other. The locomotives disintegrated on impact, the firemen, some railway workers and, eventually, four passengers died. It was only by luck that a third train was prevented from running into the accident.

As with the captain of a ship or aircraft, a stationmaster was just that – the master – and what he said went. He was solely in charge of his own patch and no one had the right to overrule him. In keeping with the practice of those days, those considered responsible for the accident, in this case the two senior officers who had overruled the stationmaster's orders, were charged with manslaughter. At the trial, however, the judge threw out the case, suggesting that the officer who had disobeyed his own orders was to blame!

It was another confusion over orders that lead to a dreadful accident at Brundall on 10 September 1874. It became known as the 'Thorpe accident'. The line between Norwich and Yarmouth was still single track and the increasingly heavy traffic over the line made it a stressful job to keep trains moving as quickly as possible. A delay in one movement would have a knock-on effect for other trains in both directions. The train from London was delayed and it would be some while before it pulled into the Thorpe terminus and then pull out in the direction of Yarmouth.

Keen to use the gap caused by this delay of the London train, the inspector in charge decided to call forward the mail train from Yarmouth to Norwich. He drafted a signal, but then there was a discussion about running a 'special' to move local travellers rather than let them wait for the London train, and the signal was not released. In the event the London train arrived and subsequently set off towards Yarmouth. What the inspector did not realise until too late was that the telegraph operator had assumed that the drafted signal was to be sent, even though the inspector had not actually cleared it and released it. The message had gone and the mail train from Yarmouth was now on a head-on collision course with the train that had left Thorpe Station.

The crash was horrific. The two trains met with an impact that some people living in the neighbourhood thought was a clap of thunder. Both trains were heavy, one with 14 carriages and vans and the other with 13. Both drivers probably put on increased speed in the belief that the other was waiting for him at the other end of the single-line stretch. It was dark and wet and finding and treating the wounded was enormously difficult. There was the grisly business of assembling body parts to try to work out how many had died. In the end there were 26 fatalities. Incredibly, the mail guard, who had been thrown clear of his van, picked himself up, went back to the wreck and collected the mail bags and walked them to Norwich Post Office. Fortunately, the crash did not actually occur on the bridge at Brundall or the loss of life could well have been considerably greater.

The motion of a single-cylinder Foster traction engine. Next to the flywheel on the left are the lidded bearing-oilers and then comes the belted pulley for the governor. Beside this there is an eccentric for the boiler feed pump and two more eccentrics for the Stephenson valve gear. Below the long regulator rod is the crank-shaft bearing for the piston rod. To the right of these are more oilers for the drive and bearing of the crankshaft. In front there is a ratchet-worked cylinder-oiler and next to it the spring-loaded safety valve. The whole motion is exposed and a ready trap for the unwary hand.

Boiler explosions were not restricted to the railways and roads. Ploughing engines in particular, put under enormous loads and strains, were particularly prone to such accidents and, as we have seen, the early steamboat service from Norwich to Great Yarmouth came to an explosive end in 1813 when the boiler on the boat exploded, destroying the boat and claiming a number of lives.

As is often the case, many accidents were the result of stupid or thoughtless actions by people who should have known better. Riding on goods or ballast wagons was strictly forbidden, but two track workers ignored the rules near Lakenheath in 1847 and opted to hitch a lift on the ballast wagon. An axle on the wagon collapsed and the following wagon mounted the damaged vehicle and crushed the two workers to death.

The primitive load-handling equipment and the enormous weights of rail and locomotive components caused a large number of injuries and fatalities – usually when someone was taking liberties with the rules. Several workers were killed and injured as a result of trying to mount or depart from a moving train or locomotive.

Clothing might be caught on some projection, or a foot trapped, and the unfortunate employee or passenger would be dragged under the wheels of an engine. At best he might lose a limb, at worst the accident was fatal.

The devastating result of a boiler explosion on a ploughing engine in 1918. The boiler has simply disintegrated, leaving the tubes exposed. The engine has collapsed almost into its constituent parts.

Away from the railways, accidents were also frequent, but in general the effects were less dramatic. The operation of any steam engine was a dangerous occupation. The regulations that govern machinery today had not been introduced and it was only through the accidents of these early steam workers that the need for legislation became apparent. Wheels, gears and hot surfaces were all too accessible. The opportunity to lose a finger or a hand was great. Many of the drivers or machine operators were killed by the engines they operated, either by entanglement in the moving parts or through boiler explosion. Frequently, boilers were poorly maintained.

Manufacturing standards had improved as the potential dangers were realised and the failure of a new engine was highly unlikely. By the second half of the nineteenth

A Burrell having run out of control.

century the engineering standards were remarkably high and the engines produced were reliable and sound. Those engines that worked on the roads became increasingly subject to inspection to ensure that the maintenance standards were retained, although those working on the farms were not subject to the same regulations. Corners would be cut in maintenance and the wear in valves and working parts, and the subsequent loss of power, led to many malpractices on the part of the farm operators. The water used in the engines was often dirty. Furthermore, the different effects of different types of water had not been fully

This Fowler traction engine and trailer were unwelcome visitors.

appreciated, and the hard water of many parts of Norfolk and Suffolk meant that tubes and pipes tended to 'fur up' more quickly than elsewhere. This further exacerbated the loss of power.

Engines, especially those that were used on the farms, tended to be selected from the bottom end of the range available – the farmer could not afford to buy anything more. Instruments such as pressure gauges were relatively rare and the safety valve was really the only means of knowing when a boiler had reached a high pressure. Unfortunately, the safety valve was also adjustable, resulting in many operators compensating for the loss of power by increasing the pressure within the engine.

Watlington in Norfolk was the scene of an horrific accident in 1867. Two brothers of the Failes family and two others were killed when the boiler on their steam ploughing engine exploded, killing the four of them instantly. Subsequent investigation found that the safety valve had been screwed too far down, although it was never established whether this had been by accident or whether one of the operators had made the adjustment deliberately. Similar accidents occurred in some engines when the fusible plug, a further safety device, had failed. This was usually because the plug had blown on some earlier occasion, a spare had not been readily

A Burrell engine fails to take the corner. Momentum, and therefore the force needed to stop a vehicle, is a factor of speed and weight. It is unlikely that this engine was doing more than three mph and so the weight of the machine, probably about 12 tons, can be appreciated in the damage it has caused to this substantial obstacle.

available and an iron bolt or plug had been used. It might have been ignorance, it might simply have been laziness, but the effect was lethal.

Steam ploughing brought other dangers and an operator would learn to fear the 'singing' of the cable. It is a phenomenon well known to seamen, that a cable starts to emit a piercing wine shortly before it snaps. An alert operator might have time to release pressure, but several did not and the cable would snap and snake back to decapitate the operator or simply cut him in half.

An ingenious tilting plough that eliminated the need to turn the plough at the end of each furrow, but just look how exposed the crew were should the cable have started to 'sing'. Their chance of managing to get out of reach of the broken cable, as it snaked through the air, was very small.

The practice of dropping the front wheels of ploughing engines into the edge of a ditch, to prevent the engine from slewing while it was under load, also lead to a few accidents, when the operator misjudged the edge of the ditch or the firmness of the ground and the engine toppled over.

On the roads, where legislation was introduced to help protect the public, boiler explosions were rarer but by no means unprecedented. However, on rough and greasy or muddy roads there were cases of the operator losing control on a hill and the engine running away. The sheer mass of the engine was a much greater factor than speed in the damage caused wherever the runaway came to rest. Such accidents tended to occur on the descent of hills where the driver had remained in too high a gear and the heavy load became the driving force, pushing the 'train' downhill.

Accidents to engines going uphill were less common. If the road was too greasy to achieve traction, the load had to be split and taken up in two separate journeys. This in itself led to a few accidents when the unhitched part of the load was left on a slope without being adequately braked or 'scotched'. Soft edges to roads also led to several incidents where the operator, driving too close to the edge of the road, found himself in the ditch. Other recorded causes of runaways include the loss of a driving pin and the steering wheel coming off!

The traction engines were enormously heavy compared with horse-drawn carts and carriages and the roads and bridges were not built to withstand the loads. In many cases a traction engine simply disappeared through the bridge it was attempting to cross.

The potential for accidents to happen and the scale of accidents when they occurred meant that the steam engine faced a lifetime of constant struggle with legislation and taxation. Severe restrictions were placed on the times during which steam engines could use the roads and the tolls charged were high. In 1830 Goldsworthy Gurney complained to Parliament about these excessive tolls and a special committee was set up in 1831 to study the operating rules for steam engines on the roads.

The committee recommended that carriages could be driven by steam on the public roads at speeds of up to 10mph, and that they could carry up to 14 passengers at this speed. They noted that weight of an engine (including fuel, water and operators) might be under three tons and that the engines were well capable of dealing with the gradients on the public roads. They regarded steam engines as being 'perfectly safe for passengers' and that they were not in any way a nuisance to the public. The committee foresaw that they would become faster and cheaper than

Indignity as diesel rescues steam.

the horse and that, because they had a wider footprint on the road, they did less damage than a series of horses passing constantly down the same track in the road. In view of this the committee agreed that the tolls charged were excessive.

The report was much more favourable than almost anyone had predicted, but it was only the report of a committee and it had no force in law and very little was done after the report had been presented. The timing was perhaps wrong because the Reform Act of 1832 was also in the process of being introduced and this rearranged constituencies and brought the vote for the first time to large numbers of relatively wealthy, middle-class people. In this period Turnpike Acts continued to be passed and there seemed to be a genuine wish to tax the steam engine off the road. Parliament seemed uninterested in any opposition to this policy and one of the key reasons seems to be that the turnpike trusts were in the hands of the gentry, who disliked the change that the steam engine represented. Certainly, after the agricultural problems of the Napoleonic period, many rural landowners were concerned that the steam engine would spell the end of their trade in animal fodder and bedding.

But sometimes the boot was on the other foot. Here, at Waldringfield, a Fowler pulls a Commer truck out of the ditch as late as July 1966.

It was a short-sighted view which might have been more understandable if the opposition had come from the railway companies, scared of competition from road transport. In 1836, the House of Commons did at last pass a bill to relieve steam engines of the exorbitant taxes, but the House of Lords, very much the fortress of the gentry, rejected the bill.

Possibly the success of the railways and the speed of their construction helped to impede road transport because a good, reliable, fast alternative was being created. This not only argued against making it easier to operate on the roads, but it brought with it a strong lobby from the railway companies who now wanted no competition. The Locomotive Acts of 1861 and 1865 seemed at first sight to be the relief that the road operators sought. The excessive tolls were removed and there were practical provisions for the construction and weight of road steam vehicles.

Unfortunately, the Act then specified a number of restrictions that made operation of a road transport system all but impractical. Highway engineers and surveyors were given the right to prevent steam engines from using any bridge that was not, in their opinion, strong enough. This seems a sensible precaution, but it was left to a matter of opinion rather than engineering fact. Further, the Act provided that if a steam engine caused any damage to the road or a bridge then the operator would be responsible for the cost of the repair (no such penalty was imposed on horse-drawn transport). The Act also stated that all steam engines must consume their own smoke.

On the road a man had to walk 60 yards ahead of the steam engine to warn oncoming horse traffic that a steam engine was approaching, and this person had to assist in controlling the horses while the steam engine passed. It also became illegal for the operator to allow the safety valve to blow on the public road. The speed limits were set generally at two mph in the towns and four mph elsewhere. Finally, the Act gave power to local authorities to decide the hours of the day that steam engines could use the roads. This was a power that was widely abused and some local authorities made it virtually impossible to operate a steam transport system on the roads. Even moving a ploughing engine to the right field for the day's work might mean a move that had to be undertaken before 6.00am. If the journey was an hour and it took perhaps two hours to steam up, it was a very early start from home for the ploughing team, especially if they had to wait until after 8.00pm to make the return journey. Eighteen-hour working days were quite usual.

This was probably the nadir of the steam engine and successive Acts over the next thirty years gradually eased the restrictions. The Locomotives and Highways Act of 1896 recognised that the new steam cars and lighter traction engines could not be treated in the same category as those engines designed for heavy haulage. The need for a three-man crew was dropped and the speed limit raised to six mph.

The enforcement of the law over the second half of the nineteenth century saw many convictions for excessive smoke, blowing off steam, obstructing other traffic, and claims for damages and excessive wear. However, eventually the burden of legislation was relaxed and a more equitable balance was achieved, matching the needs of safety and nuisance reduction with the clear advantages that steam haulage could bring to all communities.

Chapter Nine

The Decline of Steam Power

A t sea the last phase of the Steam Age was perhaps its most glorious. In 1899 the Royal Navy had destroyers that were capable of 37 knots. Liners such as the *Mauritania* and *Queen Mary* were in service, with the massive turbines on *Queen Mary* capable of developing up to 100 000 horsepower. However, fuel oil had started to become available in usable quantities and for the Royal Navy this was a considerable benefit. Coal smoke was a great obstacle to surprise and gave away the position of the fleet long before it appeared over the horizon.

The logistics of running a coal-powered Navy were quite awesome. During the First World War, the battleship *Orion*, for instance, burned over 350 tons of coal a day. Multiply that by the number of ships in the Royal Navy over the four years of war and it represents a staggering amount of coal. It was not surprising that oil became the preferred fuel and, as soon as the diesel engine became effective, it was the natural and inevitable successor to the steam engine at sea.

It had taken many years for steam to reach something like its real potential at sea and, in oil-burning form, steam was to remain in maritime use until the middle of the nineteenth century. Often this was simply because the old construction methods for steam engines had been so robust that owners were reluctant to invest in anything new when they had a perfectly serviceable engine in use. It was only when taxes started to bite on fuel oils that the real need for fuel economy was highlighted.

Awaiting scrap in 1964.

A ploughing engine awaiting an enthusiast to love and restore it.

On land, for a long while there was never any real incentive to progress from the traction engine. Labour and coal were relatively cheap and traction engines served the haulage and agricultural sectors well. Coal was ten shillings a ton and there was no shortage of manpower to operate the machines. There was no great incentive to explore new technologies or even try to make significant improvements on the old. Methods of construction were labour-intensive but modern techniques and production lines were not forced onto the engineering industry.

However, the advent of the diesel or paraffin engine and the tractor was the start of the decline of steam. The tractor was inherently safer to operate, it could be started from cold and ready for work immediately, and it could be stopped whenever required. Amongst a number of firms in England, who might have grasped the new technology and turned it to their advantage, were Garrett of Leiston and Clayton & Shuttleworth, also of Leiston. However, both companies had invested heavily in developing their market in Russia and both were owed large sums of money at the time of the Russian Revolution. The new government in Russia conveniently walked away from these debts and with it they effectively removed the capacity for Garretts or Clayton & Shuttleworth to invest in new technology.

Efforts were made to try to merge some of these companies into a viable consortium. In East Anglia a merger was attempted with Garretts, Charles Burrell, Aveling & Porter, Davey Paxman and others. It might have worked had there not been so many vested interests and so much internal rivalry. The effect was that by the time of the First World War only Sentinel was left in England developing steam-engine design.

The flood of ex-military machines onto the market in 1918 was a contributory factor to low investment. These machines were relatively cheap and many hauliers and farmers were able to buy their own machines for the first time. Existing manufacturers saw little advantage in trying to compete by investing in new designs and they contented themselves with making minor improvements and modifications to their pre-1914 models.

In 1932 a further nail in the coffin of the steam engine was the introduction of much higher taxes as a result of the Salter report. Steam was in decline throughout the 1930s and would probably have died then, but for the Second Word War. After the war, diesel and petrol internal combustion engines really took over. It was still possible to find steam being used on the railways and in some specialist roles such as road rolling and pond and ditch dredging (using the old ploughing engines), but gradually steam disappeared from the daily scene.

For the next ten or fifteen years it was possible to pick up a traction engine or almost any kind of steam engine for its scrap-metal value. One or two enthusiasts were able to indulge in what was a relatively cheap hobby and build up collections of engines. It is doubtful if many of these would have been able to foresee the interest and the cash value placed on these machines today. A traction engine costing just tens of pounds in 1960 can easily be worth over £100 000 today.

There were many factors that contributed to the passing of steam power. Not least of these was the fact that life was often very hard. To 'fire up' and prepare

Left to rot.

Many engines were simply left at the end of a working day, never to be used again. For the restorer, such finds could be wonderful opportunities to acquire an engine in good working order, but it was always a gamble because, until the engine was stripped down, it was never really possible to assess the state of the boiler.

a locomotive or a traction engine is a time-consuming and dirty business. After the work was done, the fire had to be raked out and made ready for lighting the next morning. Fuel bunkers and water tanks had to be refilled and lubrication and maintenance carried out on the machines. The working day for operators could be very long. It was not simply the economy of the diesel and petrol engines that was in their favour, it was also the fact that few drivers at the time would mourn the passing of an onerous way of life. The ability to turn a starter motor and employ instant power made the working day more productive and much more flexible. Rising coal

Bought 'as seen and lying', in the hope that it can be put back into steam without major boiler work.

prices combined with the comparative speed, quiet and comfort offered by the internal combustion engine made it a more pleasant and convenient working partner. It was also a much safer working partner.

Perhaps the greatest factor was simply the march of technology. There was a series of advances across the whole technological spectrum, not simply in engine design. Often these advances were straight complements of each other; as roads became better so cars and trucks could achieve higher speeds in safety, and so the roads improved further. Air travel was becoming a more practical option for moving both passengers and mail, and even some freight, around the world. A steam car was produced in limited numbers and was comparatively expensive to buy. It was beyond the reach of the average working man. The petrol-engine car could be mass-produced in large numbers and at a price affordable to many working families. The very nature of the petrol engine meant that the design of the passenger-carrying part of the vehicle could be made much more comfortable and better protected from the elements. The much lighter construction enabled the development of more effective suspension. Furthermore, the vehicle could be produced in a compact and practical form and it was quite feasible to keep one in the 'shed' at home.

A 'Suffolk Punch', seen here in its restored state at Appleyard, 14 June 1954. This was built by Garrett's of Leiston and, although usable as a basic, light tractor, it was hardly practical for any other use and the growing popularity of petrol and diesel tractors prevented its further development.

Steam trucks, at their best, were fast and quiet vehicles but they still needed frequent stops for water and fuel. Even with the quick-steaming versions there was neither the flexibility nor, weight-for-weight, the power that the diesel engine could offer. A diesel engine gave greater range and greater payload; it was economic to operate and for the haulier there was really no other option.

At sea, where oil-burning steamers had replaced the older coal burners, the diesel engine again offered far better economy. Oil burners had increased the range of ships and had made many of the traditional coaling ports redundant, but the diesel engines offered far greater range still.

On land, the winter smogs of London and other major cities were driving a move towards cleaner power in transport, industry and power generation. For the railways, steam continued in service for several years after the end of the Second World War. The 1948 nationalisation of the railways was met with mixed feelings, but it was an excellent opportunity to create a truly integrated transport system. Unfortunately, subsequent legislation, in particular the 1953 Transport Act, removed many of the restrictions from road hauliers and the road industry cut prices in an effort to take business from the railways. Instead of competing, the newly nationalised railways seemed to have a death-wish, almost to the extent of discouraging freight traffic on the railways.

In the early to mid-1950s Norfolk and Suffolk lost several of their branch and minor railway lines. This rather depressing period of our railway history continued into the 'Beeching era'. Dr Beeching became chairman of British Rail in 1962 and in an attempt to rationalise and economise he further cut feeder lines on both the passenger and the freight routes on the main lines. In terms of freight, this might have been the right move, because it could in theory have lead to the wider use of container traffic and the integration of the road and rail systems to achieve door-to-

All too familiar sights on Norfolk and Suffolk railways in the mid-twentieth century.

door service, although with continuing high prices for rail transport and the need for additional handling, the preference to use road for the entire journey remains strong. This enormous reduction in the local rail network over a period of some ten years coincided with the passing of the steam locomotive and the introduction of electric- and diesel-driven services. So when we now look back at the passing of steam we tend to bring the two quite separate elements, steam and branch lines, together. We can all admire and mourn the loss of the magnificent locomotives that hauled the main-line express trains. However, for the folk of Norfolk and Suffolk, the passing of the branch lines and the link lines, with their light steam locomotives, has an arguably greater sadness. They were as much a part of the landscape as the church towers and they are still very much missed.

Now that operating these beasts of the Steam Age is not a necessity, there is a fascination to keep them alive and to demonstrate to the younger generations the power and beauty of those wonderful steam engines. In the 1940s and 1950s locomotives, industrial engines and traction engines could be seen lying around in large numbers, some awaiting the scrapyard and the re-use of their metal for more modern machines. Others were simply left to rust in the corner of a farmyard or tucked away in some forgotten barn. This was the era when, for just a few pounds, anyone with the inclination might have picked up a steam engine.

Thankfully, a few enthusiasts did just that. For many it was the chance at last to own one of these amazing machines, perhaps the one they had spent most of their

Ploughing engines, traction engines, portables, trucks and rollers. Part of the collection preserved at Bressingham Steam Museum.

Keeping one another going in retirement!

working life on and had never dreamed of being able to afford it. Now it was redundant and cheap and the operator could take it home and care for it as a hobby, just as he had cared for it for the many years of their shared working life. Others started to collect. It might have been the chance find of an old steamroller or traction engine when they purchased their farm, or it may have been a deliberate purchase to start the collection, but for those with a modest amount of cash to invest, steam engines of all sorts were there to be bought.

The result is that today, all around the country, and especially in East Anglia, we have some wonderful, preserved collections of the Steam Age and the history that is associated with it. Major annual events such as the Rougham Steam Fair and the Weeting Rally attract large numbers of steam enthusiasts who bring their engines to display with evident pride and satisfaction. The public also flock in large numbers to these events and it is quite common to see grandfather or great-grandfather telling the youngsters all about life in the Steam Age.

However, the fascination is not going to stop with the passing of the last of those who lived and worked in the Steam Age. Today, these collections are nurtured and operated by a new generation of steam enthusiasts, people who have never known these machines as anything but museum exhibits and the centre of a fascinating hobby.

Of course, in the Steam Age it would have been very rare to see a female operator. This was once almost exclusively a male preserve but today it is quite common to see ladies taking their place on the footplate and driving traction engines and railway locomotives. Male or female, almost all of these are volunteers. They do it for the love of steam and the fascination of the engineering. Certainly, each society has its social side that helps bind it together, but the central pull is the machinery itself.

The question that faces many of these organisations today is how long they can survive. A love of steam engines and operating and engineering skills are not enough. Year on year it is becoming an increasingly expensive hobby. The only way many enthusiasts can afford to enjoy it is to share or to join a museum or operating society. Unfortunately it is unlikely to become any cheaper. Quite rightly, there is a high regard for safety and the Pressure Vessels Regulations demand that boilers are inspected at frequent intervals with major overhauls every seven years (possibly extendable to ten years in some cases).

Boiler work is expensive because the boilersmiths and the large Steam Age works of yesteryear no longer exist. Every boiler overhaul is a specialist job and can be a major expense. For instance 'Royal Scot' which ran in steam at Bressingham until a few years ago, is currently going through a restoration, thanks to some generous assistance from the Heritage Lottery Fund. The costs are likely to be in the order of £300 000, with the boiler restoration alone being about £130 000 – and the boiler happens to be in very good condition.

A boiler stripped down for inspection in the workshops.

Plenty of steam in the early days at Bressingham.

Volunteers at work on Thundersley *at Bressingham. This 71-ton locomotive saw service on the London, Tilbury and Southend Railway. Although a highly successful design, it did have one major problem. The weight of the locomotive is very much towards the rear, and the lightly loaded front bogie had a habit of becoming derailed when it was shunting. The answer was to mount a pair of transverse jacks on the front buffer bar and the driver and fireman could then jack up the locomotive and wind it across and back on to the tracks.*

Even smaller projects can swallow up the money and the restoration of the Sentinel timber tractor at Bressingham cost some £8000 and a small 'Terrier' tank locomotive some £25 000. If these engines can not be put to passenger use to generate revenue, then the costs of restoration every seven years are no longer viable.

It might not be so bad if the story stopped there, but the Climate Change Levy has further increased the cost of the day-to-day operation and, where an organisation is running a railway of any sort, the insurance costs have gone through the roof. A recent quotation for the combined liability insurance for a charity running a narrow-gauge heritage railway was over £28 000, against a premium the previous year of £7000. This is the price that anything to do with railways now has to pay for some high-profile accidents on the national rail network. These costs can be

The Flying Scotsman *hauling an enthusiasts' special through the Suffolk countryside west of Bury St Edmunds.*

daunting and there has to be a considerable body of enthusiasm and determination to overcome them.

Fortunately the attraction of steam remains. The power, the strange blend of simplicity and complexity, the extraordinary engineering achievements of the days when machine tools were very much more basic than today, all combine to provide a fascinating experience for the regular operator or the casual visitor. It is as interesting to watch those who come to see as it is to watch the machines themselves. The giant flywheel of the beam engine turns slowly round and the massive piston slides gracefully in its cylinder. That such massive engineering could have been achieved to such fine tolerances is a marvel in itself. The onlookers simply stand and watch, mesmerised by the strange beauty and awesome power that is displayed before them.

As long as volunteers can be found to operate and maintain these wonderful relics of the Steam Age, then the Steam Age will continue to flourish long after its official decline. Evidence from all around Norfolk and Suffolk is that as long as there are steam engines to operate then there will be volunteers. The Steam Age may have passed and we may all live in a cleaner, more efficient and more comfortable world, but one can only marvel at the skills and ingenuity of our forefathers who built and operated these engines and so laid the foundations of much of our modern technology.

Let us hope that common sense is balanced with practicality and the need for safety, and that the many Norfolk and Suffolk organisations dedicated to the Steam Age are not regulated and taxed out of existence.

Part of the Grand Parade of 26 saved and restored traction engines at Stistead in July 1956.